About the Author

Amy Tollyfield is a published author and performance poet. She has performed her poetry at a variety of venues in the south west of England, including Clifton Literature Festival 2019, The Barbican Theatre in Plymouth and The Wardrobe Theatre in Bristol. Her poetry has received largely positive reviews, credited for its emotional and rhythmic qualities. Amy has appeared in Mslexia, Diva magazine online, and Bristol24/7. She holds a Master's degree in Shakespeare Studies (Birmingham), a Bachelor of Arts (Honours) degree in Drama and Theatre Practice (Hull) and is a former registered member of the National Youth Theatre of Great Britain.

Photo credit: Simon Holliday, 2021

Brixton Nights

Amy Tollyfield

Brixton Nights

Olympia Publishers
London

www.olympiapublishers.com
OLYMPIA PAPERBACK EDITION

A CIP catalogue record for this title is
available from the British Library.

ISBN: 978-1-80074-514-8

This is a work of fiction.
Names, characters, places and incidents originate from the writer's
imagination. Any resemblance to actual persons, living or dead, is
purely coincidental.

First Published in 2022

Olympia Publishers
Tallis House
2 Tallis Street
London
EC4Y 0AB

Printed in Great Britain

Dedication

To any women reading this who are hurting.
Did you find your forever place? Can you still remember what
it looks like? Shall we search for it together?

Acknowledgments

I would like to thank the following individuals and organisations for their continued interest in my writing, and for their general warmth.

My parents and brother Elliot for their kindness over the last thirty years.

Olympia Publishers for their continued belief in me and my published works.

For their enthusiastic interest in my poetry and warm appreciation of my zeal: Mum, Dad, Shelley Cannings, Sian Mundy, Anne Gesell, Isobel Dams.

For their consistent friendship and kindness: Rick Nunn and Dana Paduraru.

Nataša Jović and her partner Simon Erasmus for warm, caring friendship in my hour of need.

Amy Trewick for her friendship, even when I wasn't around to feel its glow. Thank you so much.

My paternal grandmother for her kindness and continued interest in my writing.

A couple of friends of my parents who travelled all the way down from Derbyshire to Bristol to celebrate with us on the launch night of my first book. It was the best surprise. That touched my heart so much, and I will never forget that you did that.

The office manager I worked for in a small Derbyshire town

who told me to never change. I took your advice and have climbed so many tall mountains since. Thank you so much for your tough, candid feminism.

E. A., for your ready enjoyment of my poetry and for encouraging me to try to get my poems published. You made such a difference. Thank you so much.

Anyone who came to the Foyles Bristol book launch for my first book and made it such a special evening for me.

Any other friends who have shown their support, particularly those in Bristol.

Tom and Philippa Harding, and the team at *Northampton Poetry Review,* for their kind interest in my poetry.

Simon Holliday for his brilliant photography.

The team at *Bristol24/7* — both past and present — for their kind interest in my writing while I was local to Bristol.

The team at Waterstones Clifton, for hosting a fantastic launch event for my first poetry collection.

The lesbians who, like me, have spent so many painful nights dancing in the shadows of a dark, inconsequential nightclub, desperately searching for love amongst the sweat and the indifference. This is for you.

Once Upon a Time in Brixton

One of my friends
Has a coke habit,
Lives on the floor of someone else's apartment,
And struggles to hold down a job
But not a girlfriend.

Another friend says of herself
That she's a 'pragmatist' with relationships,
Doesn't understand why people want to date a woman who is
very attractive
As it will only end in heartbreak.

Friend one's girlfriend is beautiful:
Show-stoppingly so,
And loves her;
Once upon a time in Brixton,
In a dirty corner somewhere
Women held each other in a way
I've only seen friend one and her girlfriend do since.

Friend two is just jealous:
We don't have Brixton anymore,
Or dirty corners,
Or girlfriends,
So we peck at others' dreams,
Wishing we could have a girl look at us like that.

Brixton

August 1991

One of my earliest memories involves running through a field, Mum and Kyle not too far behind. Mum had used one of her 'connections' to secure us a lift to a disused industrial park outside of the city's perimeter, and out the back of that park were fields upon fields of fresh grass. The air had been clear and unpolluted. This was before the more recent shite about climate change, so a hot summer's day was a blessing and not a curse. Mind you, I was five years old, so probably wouldn't have made a great deal about climate change anyhow, and Mum certainly wasn't about to educate us on something so mundane.

Mum left Kyle and I alone for a little while on that trip, and we weren't really sure where she had gone, but when she came back, she was smiling. Not a big smile, but a genuine enough one. After about twenty minutes of running around the field, I had turned to look at Mum, and her eyes had looked sunken and hollow. Her face, normally so sweet and saccharine, turned sad beyond belief. Clocking my stare, Mum had instantly switched back to happiness, and so did I. She didn't want to leave, she told us. She wanted us to be able to run around the field forever.

I wasn't sure quite why she felt like this. Our place wasn't too bad. It was damp and quite smelly, but we survived, and we were happy together as a threesome. We lived in an apartment complex on Temple Close in South Brixton. It wasn't one of these godawful skyrise blocks, but a neat enough three-storey building in a quieter corner of the bustling London suburb. We'd attended a decent enough primary school for our first couple of years of education, and Mum got on relatively well with the neighbours. I don't really know what anyone else can expect from their childhood — we never went massively without, nor were we living the life of luxury, either.

This is where Kyle shakes me awake: where we swap roles and I become the younger sibling rather than older, where the distortion of memory risks diluting our shared history altogether. He reminds me of the nights at Simone's when I held him as he wept as quietly as possible into my armpit, or the times we went into Mum's room in the early hours to find — Kyle, what did we find? Kyle?

For now, though, it's August of 1991, and we aren't so bad. Our father left Mum a long time ago, just a few months after Kyle was born. I'm five and Kyle is four. We are only eleven months apart in age. From what I know of Mum and our father's relationship when he was around, it was volatile. My father was violent. Sometimes, when Kyle got angry, Mum would shake with fear. We weren't sure if that was a sincere reaction or not, looking back, as Kyle was only four years old. She'd tell him to not be anything like his father, and me nothing like her, either. She already knew I was going to be very different, I think, as she laughed at me a lot and told me I was 'bright but an odd one.' She named me after Tina Turner, she said. A song that came out the year before I was born, Mum's new favourite. 'What's Love Got to Do with It'. She used to blast it out regularly on her bright pink

CD player when we were little. Mum didn't like the name 'Tina', thought it sounded too common, but 'Christina' she could get behind. I'm not sure who Kyle was named after, if anyone.

The summer heat burnt Brixton to a near crisp, and the older boys next door used to spend hours kicking their football against our broken fence, driving Mrs Crabby downstairs to melting point. She used to boil up like a kettle. Her name wasn't actually Mrs Crabby, of course, but Mum used to call her that, and Kyle and I used to laugh every time she said it. Mrs Crabby was actually of Pakistani-Indian descent, with a real name of Mauvinder, though goodness knows what her real surname was. I'm doubtful it was 'Crabby'. She used to sing very untunefully in the mornings, so Mum would turn the radio up as loud as possible to drown out the awful singing. Mum and Mrs Crabby didn't especially get on, but Mrs Crabby appeared slightly frightened of Mum, so never did anything about it. Mrs Crabby didn't seem to have any family, and no one really came to visit her, though she was a nice enough lady. I wasn't sure of her age at the time, though looking back I would guess that she was possibly around sixty-five when I was five. I suppose it is quite unusual now, looking back, for a Pakistani-Indian woman to live alone at the age of sixty-five in the UK. Isn't it? Mrs Crabby would be one of the vast plethora of women I met in my life who were unusual in some way, but who, for whatever reason, I never really understood or fully connected with. Women can be vague like that.

Mrs Crabby used to leave her back door wide open sometimes, and we would peer in from the yard. She was never really doing anything of note. Sometimes she would be crocheting. If she caught us staring, she would smile, but never speak and never invite us inside. We know she could speak as we heard her mumbling to herself a lot, and of course singing. Her home — what we saw of it from the kitchen doorway — was just as dirty as ours. She often cooked vegetables rather than meats, and the smell was lovely, but having seen the inside of her home, and certainly her kitchen, one wonders how hygienic her food preparation habits were.

Above us were a young Polish couple, and occasionally we heard the man shouting at the woman, and sounds of him hitting her, and her screaming. Mum said not to worry. Mum said that if they were doing it to each other then they wouldn't do it to us, and also that they'd pay less attention to what we were doing if they were so embroiled with each other. What were we doing anyway, Mum?

This particular Sunday afternoon we were not doing much. Mum had brought us back from the field and given us an ice lolly each. I had the rocket one, Kyle had a Mr Freeze. I was older so I got the better one. We turned the telly on and sat down to watch endless repeats of *The Golden Girls*. I wasn't really sure why Mum liked this show, as it was very boring. Nonetheless, we were happy enough to sit with Mum and watch. We didn't have a vast number of toys, so it was better than sitting on our own in our room. This Sunday, Mum had an idea: we should prank Mrs Crabby.

Poor Mrs Crabby. She had gone out to collect her weekly grocery shopping, which she painfully did on foot (I'm sure the bags were heavy to carry home, with the thin plastic bag handles cutting into the tired skin on her hands), as none of the residents in our apartment block had a car. Mum had seen her waddle off down the street and round the corner at the end on to the main road and seized her chance. As I was the oldest out of Kyle and I, it was my duty to pull off most of the prank. I was not a willing participant. Mum countered that my love of Action Men toys and badass name should make me harder and better at things like this.

'Chrissy-Wissy,' she goaded, 'It's high time you live up to your rock and roll name.'

Mum never told us much about her background, but she was no idiot. Mum had natural intelligence if she had no documented intelligence, and an ability to arrange a situation to her liking that I have not seen matched since. She got what she wanted, I used to think, all of the time.

'You're my daughter or you're no one's.'

I'm not sure how much Mum registered of me at five. I'm not sure how much Mum saw of my future. One time she told Kyle and I that the only person she had ever truly loved romantically had been another woman, 'with a stiff-collared shirt to rival any bollockless man'. She had gripped my shoulder hard at this point in the story, and soothed, 'There are still some of them out there.' It did reassure, but then Mum seemed to tell so many lies that it was hard to know what was true and what wasn't. We never asked any questions; Mum was quick to move on with most of her tales. If she could spin us a yarn now — if only — I wonder what sort of crap she would drag up from the mires this time. Spin us one last tale, Mum. One last swansong of shit.

'You take this bucket,' Mum said, handing me a large, blue pail, 'And when she opens the back door, you let her have it.'

Mrs Crabby always came in through the back door. Mum said it was because she was afraid of the neighbour's dog. Again, like many of Mum's utterances, there was nothing to quantify or measure the truth of this hypothesis — nothing at all. If anything, Mrs Crabby looked like the sort of woman who would love dogs, and the neighbour's dog was several feet away, behind a deep crosswire fence, with a yappy bark that even a slow, old lady like Mrs Crabby would probably find endearing. The dog was there to ward off unwanted visitors, however it wasn't a very large dog and it didn't look like it would put up much of a fight.

The worst part of the whole 'bucket prank' affair was that we all knew Mrs Crabby would not take Mum on. She never took Mum on.

'You've got to fill it first,' Mum pressed, as if the act required any further clarification.

Dutifully, I went to fill up the bucket.

A millennium passed before Mrs Crabby returned. During that time, Kyle had tormented a spider and I had watched the several neighbourhood cats scrap with each other. The sky was getting darker now and a thunderstorm loomed. The sky around where we lived often turned darker quite quickly and, bar this particularly hot, summer afternoon, and August 1991s blazing summer heat in general, my memories of Mum's area were mostly of depressingly grey skies and overflowing bins. The street was a fairly crowded street, despite being quieter than the rest of the busy suburb, and the terraced houses next to our apartment building lined up, fence to fence, life to life. The cats would race down the fences in unison, pigeons bolting into the sky. It was the kind of street where, unless you lived there, you really didn't care what was going on, and neither did the council.

Eventually, after an age, we heard the shallow sounds of a thin key turning in a back door lock. Mum galvanised from her late afternoon slump. 'Kids,' she whispered, between laboured breaths, 'Bucket time.'

I slithered to the back window as slowly as possible. The bucket was ready and prepared. I swallowed hard, and Kyle pretended not to notice what was going on, fiddled with one of his Matchbox cars. I hesitated, the window ajar, the bucket edging closer to its moment. I slid the bucket through the crack; Mrs Crabby paid no heed. I didn't want to do this, and Mum could tell, so quick as a fox she nudged my elbow, and the bucket tipped, down, down, cascades of water, flooding the elderly lady, drenching her skin, head to toe. You wonder — of what little you already knew of her life — what this incident reminded her of, and in that moment, I thought, is Mum a racist? Is this a racist attack? Are we bullying Mrs Crabby?

A new millennium passed — longer than the first, longer than the initial wait for Mrs Crabby. This millennium was worse: I could feel the minute details of every second, the painful realisation of Mrs Crabby's wounded pride coupled with what I'd done. Well, what Mum had done. As the water had splashed around Mrs Crabby, making slapping noises on the hard concrete, the pigeons had bolted again, into the sky, and the cats, ever vigilant, chased down the fence lines, away from the scene of the crime. I could feel Mum's excited smile on my cheek as she hovered expectantly over my shoulder, both of us looking down, anticipating Mrs Crabby's next move.

Mrs Crabby was wise to this. She knew to delay. Her head raised itself slowly, belligerently, indignantly. She eventually locked eyes with me. A second or two passed, then she muttered something in Hindi, a curse of some kind. It was said only to me, her eyes wild with anger and hurt. She shot inside, and we let the curse linger in the stale air for a moment or two. The clouds above formed, the heavens opened, and we closed the window tightly shut. Once closed, Mum let out a belly laugh to rival even the most enthusiastic audience response to a stand-up comedy act.

'Amazing,' she credited me, 'You are the best.'

I was shaken by the Hindi curse, but Mum let it roll off her shoulders and onto the dirty carpet floor.

'Pay no mind to that strange wittering she came out with,' Mum soothed, 'She can sing and speak in English because we've heard her. We can't even be sure that what she said made any sense in any language.'

Mum continued to chuckle to herself and poured herself a stiff drink. The rest of the afternoon, like the downpour outside, was to continue in a dreary, dragging fashion, like it always did on Sunday afternoons, with Mum falling asleep in a drunken stupor on the single sweaty-black PVC sofa we owned, and Kyle and I making our own beans on toast for dinner.

We barely saw Mrs Crabby after that. She didn't sit with the back door open anymore, and she never smiled at Kyle and I again.

Hull

November 2019

I moved to Newcastle of all places around ten years ago. I'd just wanted to get away from Brixton and all the bad memories there, and Newcastle had a notoriously good nightlife, infamous throughout the land, so I thought, why not go there? Why not get as far away from Brixton as possible, the other end of the country? I had a wild, few years in Newcastle, made friends easily, worked a regular factory job and partied most evenings. I still managed to (somehow) stay off the drugs while in Newcastle, but the booze would flow freely and regularly.

I had to almost entirely quit the booze four years ago. My South Shields GP at the time (a crusty, old Asian man but nice enough — bit of a wandering eye but no malice with it) told me that if I kept going at that rate then I couldn't expect to live into old age as my liver was getting a real kicking. That knocked a bit of sense into me, and I've been (mostly) teetotal ever since, genuinely. I say mostly because sometimes I still allow myself the odd drink or two, but such times are a rarity. Maybe twice a month now, tops. It used to be four, sometimes five times a week!

Changing my lifestyle also involved changing my life and removing myself from the tempting haunts of the Newcastle nightlife. I moved to Hull in summer 2016 and I've been here ever since. I have nice digs here and I haven't looked back once. Hull gets a bad rep but it's been good for me. The 'arse' of the UK, it's situated on the east coast of England. You don't really go there unless you're going to the much nicer seaside town of Scarborough.

I invested in therapy not so long ago, to cope with the huge backlog of grief and trauma I had been dealing with. It took me a long time to get over my ex-girlfriend Steph. Every so often a message would pop up on Instagram or Facebook from someone from the Brixton days, and it would be immensely triggering for me. Steph would never message, but sometimes it was one of our mutual friends. It brought up a world of difficulty for me, even to just read an innocent 'hi how are you' message, so I knew I had to talk it all through with a professional ASAP.

Understanding why Steph might have left me for a man took years to process. In many ways our sex life had simulated a heterosexual relationship, so what was missing? What did he give her that I didn't? Was it a physical aspect that I was missing, or did Steph just need to be in a relationship more acceptable to society? Or was it simply me — was I not the person, man or woman, that she needed? It ate me up all through my time in Newcastle, and I took to drink and good times to take the pain away. Most Saturdays I'd be back in the toilet cubicle of some dirty nightclub, pleasuring a girl against the cubicle door. This was no life. This was no way to go.

My place in Hull was nice enough. Hull as a city was, and is, reasonably shoddy-looking but I had a nice terraced house on Albion Street. Albion Street was a quiet residential street that ran off the main road between the city centre and the university. At the bottom of the street was Princess Park which was a wide, open grassland. The park was well-maintained and good for walking dogs. I had a dog now — Baxter — and it was good to walk him there in the evenings and on the weekends. I still didn't technically own my house, it was a rental, like before; but it was good to have it and I had free licence from the landlord for pets, decorating, guests etc. I slowly made the place my own: painted a little, hung up the portrait of the white deer from Steph, invested in some new furniture. I'd long since sold off most of the furniture I'd shared with Steph years ago, and there were some great local charity shops on the high street which were good for furniture, clothes, and random ornaments. I now had five Buddhas, each from a different charity shop in Hull, each a different colour, size and material, and three lemon lime dracaenas (a type of houseplant).

I liked Hull as a place. The locals are really nice. There is some trouble but mostly the troublemakers are 'yobbish' rather than out-and-out malicious. The sun seems to shine well in Hull; there isn't a lot of rain. I like the flatness of the terrain: it makes it much easier to go for long walks with Baxter. A lot of the buildings are boarded up — especially old pubs that clearly would have been very beautiful in their Victorian heyday — which is sad to see but also fairly unsurprising. It's a coastal conurbation with a low employment rate. Bransholme, in East Hull, was at one point believed to be the largest single council estate in Europe. So, there are issues here. But it has a thriving gay scene (I think), and people have always been friendly to me, so I've no complaints. From the raucous lifestyle I had in Newcastle it's a welcome respite, and there are plenty of lesbians here, from what I've seen, and they aren't half-bad to look at or talk to. So, I've cashed my chips, at least for now.

Not too long ago there was a murder in Hull. A female student. I don't often feel frightened for myself but recently I had been. I don't often feel 'female' as such, but when something like that happens, you start to feel aware of your body and your gender. Now I felt very aware of it, and took steps to make myself safer. I carried a personal alarm about, even when just walking Baxter in the day, and triple-checked my doors and windows at night, before I went to bed. In this sense I developed slight 'OCD' tendencies, but it was better that than feeling unsafe.

I replaced the addiction to alcohol with an addiction to working out. I took steroids for a while and became slightly hooked on protein shakes. My partiality to protein shakes I've retained; the steroid addiction had to go, though. At my worst my arms were like two great sacks of potatoes. Now they are toned and strong and bulky without being too much. The rest of me is big and bulky, too. I've never been tall so I must look quite funny: like 'short man syndrome' personified but 'short lesbian syndrome' instead. I'm almost certain that such a syndrome exists.

Eventually, I've been able to cut back on having to have any kind of addiction. I still go to the gym sometimes, but not nearly as often as I used to, and the steroids have of course gone. Therapy has done a world of wonder to help me learn to just exist, without so many compulsive behaviours or outlets thrown into my daily life.

I've a decent collection of sex toys in the corner of my bedroom that every so often get a dusting off and a chance to prove themselves. I've a large, master bedroom with a king-size bed so that's good. Money goes far in Hull and digs are cheap. I've always lived in the same place but from what I understand, I could get an even bigger place if I wanted, on my wage. But I'm frugal, and I have nice neighbours. I'm the noisiest, blasting dubstep out of my living room bay window on Sunday afternoons, and I'm not even that noisy. If it feels okay, then why change it?

From time-to-time I bring a girl back from one of the local clubs and that's when my toys get the opportunity to shine. I used to be too shy to use them but now I think, why wait? I've never been one to receive so I quickly mark the lines — draw the picture in the girl's head at the bar — what I am about and what I want to do to her. Most girls are keen, occasionally one or two will want to reverse things up. I'm not into that; I've always been the top. If she wants to find a bottom for herself then there are plenty of them out there.

It's taken a lot of practice to get good at wearing a strap-on, but I've got there and now I would say I'm pretty damn good. The rhythm is hard to get right: I find it easiest if a girl sits on top of me, facing me. Still hasn't found me a girlfriend, though, as casual sex usually won't do for anyone. I miss intimacy, secrets, closeness, warmth, sharing a bed regularly. Christ, I miss Steph. Specifically, Steph. After all these years, I miss Steph. How can I still miss her after all this time? But I do.

I work in a pea-canning factory. I've worked in it since I moved to Hull. Again, if it isn't broke etc. etc. Some of the men are a bit arseholey. One or two of them seem to find me amusing in some way. That's hard sometimes. But generally, they are okay. It is mostly men. I have a friend or two among them; one is a straight guy named Bobby. 'Bobby' of all names. What straight guys do you know called Bobby? Well, I know one, and work with him. Sometimes we'll go for a beer together after work, which is an especially nice pastime in the summer months. There are some good pubs near to the factory, and most pubs in Hull have great beer gardens. Again, the sun is good in Hull. It shines a lot. The landlords of Hull maximise on this, and I'm often seen outside, tanned and smiling, pint in hand. Like the band from the place, I've everything but the girl. I turned thirty-four with everything but the girl.

Brixton

June 1993

We'd been with Mum's friend Babs for three months when social arrived to take us elsewhere. Mum claimed that Babs was her 'sister' however they looked nothing alike (Mum had fiery red hair and black eyes; Babs had very dark hair and grey eyes), Babs was considerably older than Mum (or certainly looked it), Babs spoke with what I can now in hindsight discern as a thick Liverpudlian accent (why was she in Brixton? What was her past? What was Mum's?), and finally, most importantly, Babs was unequivocally and objectively an 'ugly' woman, where Mum was beautiful.

Mum was beautiful. The day we'd left her flat, 15th March that year, I'd found her, cocooned in her bed, eyes wide open. There were gashes in her face and blood on the sheets. I'd taken in the room quickly: several empty bottles, a credit card on the upturned wicker bin she'd morphed into a makeshift side-table, a half-snorted line of white powder. Her hair had been fanned out around her, bountiful curls of bright red hair, her ample breasts spilling out of the thin duvet. It feels weird to remember her breasts, so in my mind I cover them back up with the duvet, correct the mess. I tidy the room, pick up the dirty lingerie, remove the scars and take out the waste.

Mum's make-up was still pristine, it always was. Her small mouth pursed below a reasonably sized nose. Her nose was not so large that it was out of place, but slender, and in keeping, joining together a delicate, oval face.

She noticed me too late: I'd already taken in the room, gulped it in, willingly, to understand Mum's life. She seethed and bubbled at my supposed judgment. 'Out,' she hissed, 'Now.'

That afternoon, 15th March, after school (we'd finally been back there after a week or two of non-attendance), Babs came to collect us. Babs didn't drive either, so she made sure to hold our hands tightly on the way home, Kyle on her left, me on her right, lest we run off. Babs was quite a rotund woman and had the misfortune of laboured breathing, constantly. I wouldn't wish to be ungenerous to her memory, but she was quite a comical figure, really. Her unfortunate appearance and her deep, manly voice and her large gait were all suggestive of bad luck; of a God-creator figure who'd had a laugh when he'd made her.

Babs, like Mum, spent a lot of time drinking. She was heavily tattooed and accustomed to napping on her sofa. Babs' flat, much like Mum's, had a single, sweaty-black PVC sofa and the same dull, whitewashed walls. Babs' flat was actually worse in terms of ornamental value than Mum's: Mum at least had a couple of vintage-style frames put up, displaying gravy adverts from the 1960s. Babs seemed to have zero taste at all — no decoration, nor a lone magazine in sight. Nothing. The skies around Babs' place were similarly dark and gloomy. During our time with Babs a young black man was killed in a racially motivated attack on the streets of London, adding to the gloom. It made national news, and made the city tense and unfriendly for a while.

Babs was a sad but kind woman. Kyle and I would often

draw over her tattoos in green marker pen as she slept on the sofa, and when she woke up, she wasn't angry. It was as if life passed her by, and she chose not to engage with it. Life came to her; she didn't get up and go to life. We were starting to miss Mum's by the time social arrived and had made plans to return. We were only a few streets away. Mum hadn't told us why she'd made us go to Babs' place, nor how long we'd have to be there, but we knew that she'd want us back eventually, surely. The two months before we'd left, Mum had been crying a lot, and there had been an increase of unusual men at the flat. They always came alone, and we were lucky to never be touched or handled in any way, by any of them. Looking back, we were very lucky indeed.

We didn't have a shared bunkbed in a boxroom like we did at Mum's, but slept on two single blow-up beds on Babs' living room floor. There was no mistaking whose kids we were when social arrived, as we stared up at them with our charcoal black eyes. Babs let them in without a fight, gazed down at us with a solemn smile and watery eyes. In our mind Mum cried, too; cried at the thought of losing us, cried at the thought of never seeing us again. At that age, of course, we thought we would see Mum again, and that this was all temporary. Even social taking us away was temporary; it had to be.

We heard Babs exchange a few words with social; some kind of tip-off, hadn't been to school in three months, a neighbour downstairs from Mum. Mrs Crabby? What did she care if we were okay, having not smiled at us in nearly two years? Were social meant to let Babs know this kind of thing? What if Mum caught wind? What would happen to Mrs Crabby then?

There was a moment of tension, when it seemed as though social would interrogate Babs further. Babs was clearly involved in some kind of illicit trade: a brief scan of her flat would uncover drug paraphernalia without too much trouble. Babs looked shifty at best the whole time social were there and had opened the apartment door to them in pyjamas with a bottle of Lambrini in her left hand. Social eventually let it go, nodded 'thank you Barbara' and took us, just like that, in the middle of the night. If it wasn't my own life, I'd say it was some kind of story.

Social were a man and a woman — late forties both, nondescript appearances, family-type personalities. They didn't ask a lot of questions, but the female was marginally more attentive. Said they'd have us somewhere new soon enough. And with that we were whisked away in an ordinary black saloon car, and that was the end of one chapter.

* * *

We didn't wait long for a new place. The intention was that Simone would foster us with a view to adoption, but we were adopted very quickly. If not by law, then by nature. Simone was a large personality, with a big heart and a messy home. She would clean her back steps frantically, every day, splashing some kind of chemical on them and singing all the while, Jesus songs, songs about God.

Simone's home was littered with things. Whereas Mum's home had been dirty and unkempt, Simone's was just a tip full of items. Items, items, items. Wooden animals, African-looking creations. Carved figures of the Virgin Mary, carved figures of lions, carved gorillas, all set in oak, dancing around her home. The decor was a clash of colour, deep reds, indigos, mixed with dark woods. The furnishings were old and traditional, and could have made for a nice interior layout, but were spoiled somewhat by overcrowding and heavy colours on the walls. Bright designs mixed with dark lighting due to the lack of natural light in some of the rooms. It was somewhat overwhelming. A 1930s terraced, redbrick house in Northwest Brixton, Simone lived in a relatively desirable area, with good school links. We would go to a decent enough comprehensive, Kyle and I, far enough away from Mum to ensure we'd never see her or her associates again.

Simone also had red hair, though not as bright, and a lonely expression. She was full of life but also very serious and grave. On matters of religion, for instance, she was unwavering. Though a naturally warm woman, with a desire to give generously and abundantly to many, this altruicity was to prove detrimental to the ultimate goal of human existence, I feel: genuine connection with a limited number of people. For all her wonderful traits, Simone was difficult to connect with, perhaps because of how 'available to all' she was. I never approached Simone with a problem, and neither did Kyle. Instead, we would discuss it together, and be each other's sounding board. In a world where we couldn't be sure who we could trust, we could at least trust each other.

I was seven by June/July 1993, and an ideal age for starting a new school. Kyle was in an even more optimum position for learning, at a younger age than me. We both made friends fairly easily, and it was clear very quickly how bright I was. Simone, in spite of her own, self-indulgent desire to give constantly, at least looked outside of herself long enough to notice this. She encouraged me to take on additional schooling. At seven years old, this was not something I was interested in, and vehemently refused. Simone was not one to be deterred, and I ended up taking piano, tap, ballet, and additional math lessons. I didn't want this, but Simone bartered that it would all serve me well in time.

Church was compulsory on Sundays, and Simone would dress Kyle and I up in the ghastliest of outfits. Whereas Mum had let me wear Action Man trousers and tomboy clothes, Simone was not quite so understanding and had a far more conventional approach to the attire of little girls. I was kitted out in garish white pinafores with a frilly trim. Repugnant even to my memory now. I was given girls toys and teddy bears. We had a strict daytime and evening routine, with little television and certainly no *Golden Girls*. I could cope with the change, was grateful for the stable surroundings, but Kyle would itch, would scratch for something more, would want to rebel.

This would all come in time, though. For now, we had a home and a roof, and we would be okay. Simone had three cats, all of whom were ginger. She loved red hair; told us it was a gift from God. Kyle and I had not inherited Mum's red hair; instead, we both had chestnut brown hair, which we assumed must come from our unknown father.

At Sunday school I would get told off for drawing pictures of Action Men when I was supposed to be listening to the stories about Jesus and drawing Noah and his ark. The Sunday school teachers wanted to know whether I had an equally strong fascination with Barbie: I gave the wrong answer of 'no'. Kyle was very boyish and so escaped any undue analysis of his childhood gender expressions.

I had snuck a couple of my old Action Man toys into Simone's place (social had allowed it), so on Saturday afternoons Kyle and I would hide in our shared bedroom and play with them, inventing stories for them such as how they would eventually find their way back to Mum. We knew she was somewhere in the city, and we knew she couldn't be too far away. We imagined running away from school and finding her. We knew she would be missing us. At eight-thirty each evening, every evening, as Simone's cats chased each other around the house and Simone allowed herself a mere half-hour of television, indulgent as it was, Kyle would sob into my armpit. We had supposedly 'gone to sleep' but we never slept before midnight. We would tell each other stories of Mum and dreams of owning our own mobile telephones. I had the top bunk and Kyle — as the younger sibling — the bottom one, and as night drew closer, we would each make our own way to our own bunk and there continue talking, talking, talking. The night drew on and we would be talking. Mum was somewhere and she would be talking. The night came and went and in-between we had been talking, dreaming, and talking.

Hull

January 2020

I started having panic attacks around Christmas 2019, and by January 2020 I was back in therapy. This time I had a young, reasonably attractive female therapist named Lara, and she was easy to talk to and naturally receptive. She had long, dark hair and piercing green eyes. I was happy to open up to someone so beautiful. I would have guessed her age at late thirties, though cannot be fully certain of that.

Simone had been writing to me a lot recently, wanting to know how I was getting on and asking if I fancied trying out a local church. I had never, ever shown any interest in religion: why would I start now? Lara wanted to unpack the letters with me.

'How do you feel when you receive mail from Simone?' she asked, at one of our first sessions together in mid-January 2020.

'Like there's a lot more to say to her,' I replied, honestly, 'Like I want her to visit so that we can talk about more than what's in these flimsy letters.' I'd brought the letter along, and at this point in the session I waved it half-heartedly in the air, like I couldn't be bothered to physically wave the thing around, let alone read it. 'I feel like she's only giving me what I want to hear instead of opening up to me properly. I'm sick of people not opening up to me properly.'

'Good,' Lara said, affirmingly, 'That's good. Get it all out.'

So, I did. We talked about a wide range of things. Grief, loss. I wanted to talk about Steph again. For the fiftieth time, to someone new. If it wasn't while slightly tipsy at a bar it was while talking to a therapist or while queuing for lunch in the work canteen or to myself while filling up my battered, old Ford Fiesta at the petrol station. I'd always had Fords.

'And what about your own sexuality? Tell me more about that.'

That was a curveball. What is there to say. 'Well, I'm a lesbian,' I answered, bluntly, 'Is that not all there is to it?'

'Have you ever questioned your own sexuality?' She persevered. I felt preyed upon, like maybe this was some kind of Christian organisation after all and I'd been very, very mistaken in investing time and energy in this service. I looked around the bare, whitewashed room desperately for one of those 'peace-fish' symbols to confirm my worst fear: that this was a God-based therapy session, that Lara was going to force me to repent and give up on my true self, that I was going to have to join some sort of God cult. She was too pretty for therapy. This was some kind of set-up.

Peace-fish symbol I did not find, and Lara continued, 'If you don't want to talk about your sexuality, we don't have to. I just wanted to unpack a bit more about you. You're hurt that Steph left you for someone of the opposite sex. What does that mean to you? How does that influence your own sense of self or sexuality?'

It was a lot to deal with and unpack at once. I was worried the whole conversation would trigger a panic attack of an unholy, Godless scale. In the end, I was able to answer, and felt the mildly cathartic relief of being able to do so:

'I can understand the attraction to men. Men do not repulse

36

me, not even physically. I just want to be with a woman. I'm almost certain I could only ever love or be in love with a woman. It's a woman that I want to spend the rest of my life with.'

Lara smiled. 'Lifelong partnership is what so many people want. I hope you're able to find it in time. It doesn't come to all of us.' As she said this, I sighed deeply. I was turning thirty-five this year. Still young, and handsome, but getting older. Getting older and wondering when I might meet my forever girl. When my toys might not stay dusty for weeks on end, when I might be able to share dinner and romance with someone. When shit telly can be enjoyed with someone else, when we can read the newspaper together on Sunday mornings, and she can tell me off for playing too much dubstep: she prefers jazz. Maybe she'll be a jazz singer herself, with long, cascading blonde hair and a wicked smile. Maybe she'll wink like the best of them. Maybe she'll make a mean White Russian, or vodka martini, and we can stay up late, every night, drinking and laughing. Her laugh will fill the street. Her laugh will fill the city. She'll open my world, open my mind. She'll be the Venus to my Adonis. I shall want for nothing anymore. We can spend the rest of our lives together, get bored together, feel nothing and everything together, all at once.

Lara looked at me, searching my face. I was trying to smile, but a lot of me was feeling quite sad. 'Is there anyone at the moment?' She eventually ventured, 'Anyone who you feel particularly strongly about?'

There was someone new at work, an Irish lady called Siobhan. She'd started in October just gone. Siobhan had dark brown hair, olive skin and bright, hazel eyes. She was quite an electric character — a laugh that swept through the warehouse floor, an unmistakable vivacity. When we first met, she teased me on my accent. I had replied, 'Why so far from Kansas?', which she'd liked. She didn't mind a bit of friendly ridicule and gave as good as she got. I wondered if I could get her on her own time sometime, get to know her a bit, but she didn't smoke so I never saw her in the smoking area. I would have to bide my time.

I told Lara about Siobhan, and she recommended I ask her out.

'What?' I was shocked. I'd only ever asked out girls in bars, when I was fairly confident they were gay, and even then, I'd never 'asked them out', per se. It was just an offer to buy them a drink that same night, or to dance, or to come back to mine. When I met Steph, that was set up through a mutual lesbian friend of ours. We'd met at a pre-planned location, for a pre-planned date, and neither of us had had to face the awkwardness of asking the other out. So, this was new territory. Particularly considering that I worked with Siobhan, so this could go a variety of ways: sidewards, up, down, really down…

'Ask her out how?' I asked.

'For a drink,' Lara replied, nonchalantly, as though it were the most cavalier thing in the world, 'Or for food. You're a young woman, so is she. You could be going as friends for all she knows. Ask her to do something with you while not at work. Ask her as soon as you can. Why wait?'

It was a lot to absorb, but I know Lara was probably right.

'Yeh, okay,' I conceded, 'That's probably a good idea.' Lara didn't yet know my casual sex record (by this point I'd lost count of the number of women I'd slept with in my life), so in her mind I'm innocent. And in Siobhan's, too, no doubt, unless Bobby had filled her in. So, it seemed much better to hang out with a nice lady from work than continue to sleep with random girls I've only just met, right? I summarised, 'What could go wrong?'

Brixton

July 1995

We'd been with Simone for two years when we started to wonder where her money came from. She didn't work, so it seemed unusual for her to be able to afford to live. Her house was nice by Brixton standards, and she lived in a comparatively desirable area. So how did she pay for her life? Women didn't live alone much — let alone be approved by social to have someone else's kids without a husband of their own. Back then the adoption process for kids was smoother and cleaner, with more hard-done-by kids finding homes quicker and easier than these days, but still, a single woman would need to prove her keep to be eligible.

It was around this time that a letter arrived for her, so I opened it. Wrong as it was to do this, I just needed to know. She kept receiving mail in the same posh, scrawling handwriting, so I was desperate to know what was going on. Kyle was in on it too, though it was technically me who did the actual opening of the letter. Together we sat, entranced, in Simone's higgledy-piggledy kitchen, cats clawing our feet for food, devouring the letter.

It was from a man based in Norway of all places, promising to send more money soon. He also asked after us kids, wanting to know if we were okay, though this sentence seemed more of an afterthought. He wrote about church and about his life in Norway — he seemed to do a lot of cycling — and that he'd met a nice lady, five years his junior. He worked as some kind of college or university tutor.

Simone had been to an AA meeting (she wasn't a drinker, she told us, just liked the company) and came in as we were reading the letter. We shoved it down onto the table and scarpered, but it was too late. We'd read everything. Simone quickly grasped the situation as she was no fool and was firebrandingly livid. We were both grounded for three weeks, and during the third week, Simone offered us an explanation. We were taken aback by this, as Simone told us very little, and rarely opened up to us about anything.

They were technically still married, she told us, her and this chap in Norway. He originally lived over here. They were due to divorce, but she was delaying it so that she could adopt children, as it looked better if she was still married. She had caught him cavorting with his secretary (at this point sighing, 'the usual'), so he left and went to teach in Norway, while she remained in the UK. They previously lived in Reading, no kids. She let him go off with any ladies he liked in Norway, and in return he sent her money and they remained legally married. She would not remarry, she told us. He had plenty of money to send to her, she told us, as Norway was cheaper than here and he had a good job, teaching sociology to university undergraduates. When she realised that we weren't sure what 'sociology' was, she clarified, as best she could in her own, perhaps slightly limited understanding of the subject: 'study of people and societies'.

At this point she took a half-drunk bottle of brandy from the cupboard and began to pour into a tumbler, 'for special occasions only', she told us. Why was this a special occasion? She seemed sad, not happy. Was this special?

After a lengthy drink from her brandy glass, she exhaled long and hard. She didn't make eye contact with either of us for a long time, ruminated that she had told us too much, regretted it, we were too young. Neither of us spoke. I was only a few months shy of ten which was double digits, so I was surely old enough to cope with this, but I didn't say that. Simone ordered us to go to bed, and we didn't talk about any of it again, though Kyle and I of course mentioned it to each other on the sly sometimes, and we still kept an eye out for letters coming through in that posh, scrawling handwriting, which came all right, plenty and often. But we would of course never read them again.

Shortly after and without notice, Simone adopted two more children. This felt like closure: she regretted telling us the sordid details of her life so adopted more children to shut us up. Now all of the children would be ignorant together and would have to deal with not knowing much about Simone. She adopted two little black children: Elsa and her brother Darone. They were nice enough, if a little quiet and secretive, and Kyle and I played with them sometimes, though Elsa (older than Darone) was nearly three years younger than Kyle, so there was quite an age gap. In small children (under ten) the age gap is always more apparent, both in learning and in what those children might individually consider 'fun'. I was made to share with Elsa in one room and Kyle with Darone in another. As we grew older, Simone said, it wouldn't be appropriate for opposite-sex children to share a bedroom. Kyle and I were okay with this and knew she was right.

It was quickly dawning on us that Simone — with her sprawling three-storey house of cats and children — cared more for caring and giving than the lives of those she was actually caring for and giving to. What did Simone really know about each of us, and did she really care, or did she just want to care for lots of things, be needed, be loved, be essential in some way? Her husband hadn't wanted her, so maybe a hoard of cats and children might?

I'm being ungrateful. In the evenings Simone would sit alone in her living room, drinking brandy she pretended we didn't know about. She wasn't a happy woman. What women are?

* * *

It was around late September 1995 that Kyle got into his first-of-many fights at school, a real fistfight in which he'd drawn blood from another child. I'd been worried about him recently as he kept thinking that the morning post lady was Mum, come to ask for us back, and used to wait at the top of the stairs, listening intently to everything she said to Simone, their dignified, ladylike chuckles ricocheting up to the landing. As it slowly dawned on him, each time, that it wasn't Mum at the door, as she didn't laugh like that — she laughed like a hyena — let alone come round to ask for her kids back, he flew into a rage, kicking Simone's carefully-placed wooden ornaments around and punching the walls. I was the only one able to calm him down, as Simone would become very flustered, unsure of how to deal with Kyle when he acted this way, and more likely to shout and punish him rather than soothe. So, I knew Kyle was in a bad way mentally, and that something was going to happen soon. He was playing up at school, arguing with the teachers in an aggressive way and picking on some of the other kids. We'd just had the six-weeks summer holidays when the fight happened, and he'd come back to school angrier than ever.

I too made a monumental error around this time, accidentally disclosing to Simone that one of Mum's male 'friends' had once come into Kyle and I's bedroom at Mum's place and tried to talk to me, perhaps to do more, before Mum had appeared in the doorway and menacingly growled, 'don't you touch her', in no uncertain terms and, despite Mum's fairly diminutive stature, managed to scare him away from me. Kyle and I are still not sure how Mum held any sway in the situation, as the man had been very well-built. But that was Mum: she always got her way. Didn't she? What was 'her way' regards Kyle and I, did she want us gone? Did she intend for us to be taken into care, or did she want us back? When would we find out the answers to these burning, torturing questions? Mum always got her way, so was 'her way' for us to go?

Simone knew that these questions were haunting Kyle and I very deeply, and that we were both in many ways very troubled and disturbed by the last few years of our lives. She was also disturbed by my encounter with Mum's friends, insisting that 'no man should ever approach a young girl like that'. She suggested something neither Kyle nor I were anticipating at our young ages: therapy. She said it had helped her in times of trouble and now it would help us kids. I was a slightly more willing participant — albeit still confused by the prospect — than Kyle. Simone insisted that therapy should be started at a young age, in order to have maximum positive and lasting effect. Kyle reacted badly. He wouldn't talk to the therapist, and started trying to set fire to things, stealing lighters from Mr Khatri's corner shop in his efforts. This got quite serious, and Simone wasn't sure how best to deal with the situation. She invited the 'God Brigade' round (the name Kyle and I ungenerously gave to her close circle of Christian friends, mostly female) and it was agreed that Kyle would stay with a married couple for a while who lived nearby.

This was the start, rather than the end, of difficulties for Kyle and I, regards our strained relationship with Simone and her inability to discipline or even relate to either of us in a compassionate way. Something about her was naive, almost, to the ways of children and of children's minds. Certainly, from then on, I wouldn't let anything slip to her about Mum or about my past, as she was guaranteed to not understand. In fact, I wouldn't tell her anything about me or my feelings, and neither would Kyle.

* * *

My tenth birthday came and went in November 1995 and was miserable. Kyle was still living with Simone's friends and I was forced to celebrate my birthday surrounded by Elsa, Darone and some Christian children from Simone's church, all the while wearing a pretty (read: ugly) pink dress. In such company Elsa and Darone were almost fun. I'm being unkind to them, but they really were boring. They barely spoke. Kyle and I didn't know much about their past, but we'd told them loads about ours. Who even were they?

Anyway, I turned ten. Double digits. I'd made it to ten in one piece, which was quite miraculous under the circumstances. Depressed but at least alive. Simone delicately played a tune for me on her lovely spinet piano. 'Happy birthday,' she sang, with her naturally accomplished voice, 'And many blessings to you for the years ahead.' It was a kind gesture, and a far cry from the days of being cursed in Hindi.

Hull

February 2020

I hadn't yet asked Siobhan out when Darone appeared on my doorstep, for the third time in as many years. He'd been to stay before, for a couple of months at a time, and it wasn't really a problem. He'd come out as gay himself a few years ago, so we had that in common, and at just shy of thirty, I felt protective over him, almost motherly. Neither of us had a great family history, with many experiences in common, so I wanted to be supportive towards him. Simone's partner Greg had reacted really badly when Darone came out as gay in 2015, and there'd been times when Darone had sofa-surfed for months on end. I don't know what it is about gay men specifically but so many Christians seem to react much worse to knowledge of a man being gay than to hearing of a lesbian woman. I assumed this was Greg's issue, but he'd always been nice to me, so I couldn't be sure.

I had a spare bedroom in my place, so Darone could at least sleep in comfort rather than on yet another sofa. He got on well with Baxter who seemed to think a lot of him. Occasionally he also went to stay with Elsa, who now worked in HR in central London. Elsa had done really well for herself, but she and I didn't have a great deal in common. She was by now married to a stockbroker from Chelsea, for Christ's sake, and living the life of luxury. It wasn't really my thing. I preferred a more subtle way of living. I've never had a flash car or a fancy watch. It isn't my style.

From what I understand, Elsa and her husband (Tom, I believe he's called) have a penthouse apartment in Belgravia. Well! Darone stays for a few days when he visits them, but I'm not sure either Elsa or Tom are fond of him staying for prolonged periods of time. Darone is much happier coming to me, where he can relax a bit more and not be pressured too much to leave. He picks up a tiny bit of agency work when he's with me — he's worked as a cleaner for years now and it's easy to pick up cleaning work on agency — so it's not a problem. We even go to the bars together, though Darone gets very drunk and unruly when we're out, so we don't go out together masses. Once or twice, I let him bring a man home, though I much prefer if he can go to theirs. I don't overly like men in my house, though I'll tolerate it occasionally for Darone's sake. I don't make him pay me any rent when he visits, along as he sometimes contributes to the weekly grocery shop, and leaves me in peace after a month or so. It's not a bad little arrangement, though I can't help wondering where his head is at? Does he not want to settle down somewhere himself?

A couple of years ago, while drinking together in Princess Park (the first time Darone came up to stay with me), he finally revealed the circumstances behind himself and Elsa needing to go into care. They were of Afro-Caribbean heritage; specifically, both of their parents were from the West Indies. Their parents had been part of the 'Windrush' generation. Dad worked as a bus driver, Mum as a cleaner. They'd both been killed in a car crash. Elsa and Darone hadn't had any relatives in the immediate vicinity, and were taken into care for adoption. I had had a few questions at the time.

'I thought black families were usually large?' I was basing this on my own experiences of Brixton, where black and Asian families usually had relatives living on almost every other street within a 300-yard radius! Darone had sighed at my ignorance — (apparently you can grow up in somewhere as ethnically diverse as Brixton and still possess it) — and explained that his parents had emigrated alone, and that, rare for their culture, both had come from slightly smaller families anyway, from what little he knew of both of their backgrounds.

'How come yourself and Elsa didn't speak much as children?' I asked. Darone paused, contemplating his answer.

'We were both quite scarred from it all,' he responded, eventually, 'We were a really close family, and we lost our parents at a very young age.'

I guess it made sense. I had poured more whisky, and we had let the drinks take over. We did much the same now, two years later, as Darone made himself comfortable on my brown, PVC sofa, Baxter jumping up to rest beside him. He was a short, fat bulldog and I loved him. I watched him slobber all over Darone's hands.

'You can stay for as long as usual,' I reasoned, 'But if, on the rare chance, I meet someone romantically and bring her back here, you might need to go.'

Darone was happy to accept these terms, as was I. I was pleased to have his company again, at least for a little while.

* * *

It was late February 2020 when I suffered quite a vicious panic attack at my workplace. There'd been a coronavirus scare recently, all over the country. Some kind of 'Wuhan' virus. I couldn't help but laugh when Trump called it the 'China virus'. You wonder how much repressed xenophobia has to exist in one single country to elect a man like that to power. You wonder how much people have a say in any of it anyway. Either the world's gone mad, or the election process which leads up to a person like Trump being in office is a corrupt and rigged system. I suspect there are elements of both at play.

Coronavirus didn't make me suffer the panic attack. Everything is making me have panic attacks. I've been having night terrors and waking up in cold sweats. I've been experiencing all kinds of lucid dreams lately: motorbike engines revving in the background, reminding me of Kyle; Mum's laugh ricocheting through the corridors of my mind.

I sat down to breathe and struggled for the breath. Siobhan came up and handed me water. I couldn't sit down for long: I was on one of the most important conveyor belts in the warehouse. Believe it or not, I actually sort peas, pick out the duds. No, really. There are about five of us, all women, stood picking out rogue peas. You have to be quick with your eyes and hands. I've needed glasses for the very first time in the last few years and I blame it on the pea-canning factory I work in now. 100%. Nobody is meant to be that close to peas, looking at them so intently. It fucks your eyes up.

Siobhan works in HR as some kind of administrative assistant. It's like a real 'uptown girl' type love story. She is the posh, well-spoken desk jockey, I'm the pea-sorting bit-of-rough she likes. I'm getting ahead of myself. But it will keep me sane.

She traverses the warehouse floor from the first-floor office to reach the staff canteen, and it's there that she sees me, sat down, struggling for oxygen.

'Are you okay?' she asks, reaching over to put a hand on my shoulder. I'm sat on one of those school-type metal chairs, the ones that are reinforced with plastic at the back. Really uncomfortable, but littered all over the factory. 'Sorry, I don't know if people are meant to touch at the moment.' She slowly moved her hand away from me, though in a gradual manner, not too fast. 'Coronavirus and all that.'

I winced up at her. I had so many things I wanted to say. So many nights I had sat drinking alone, feeling lonely, or with Darone, talking shit. I wanted to have some company.

'Do you—' I wheezed, taking a swig of the water to propel me into reality and this very, very important moment right now. 'Do you want to hang out sometime?'

She smiled, quite naturally, showed me her front teeth, which were straight and white. Hopefully she wasn't so straight, but the question I had posed was casual and noncommittal, so either way, we could at the very least be friends.

Her answer seemed to take forever to come, and I could see from the corner of my eye that the peas were mounting up, that soon enough I'd need to return to the conveyor belt and start sorting them again, or else my boss would come along and give me hell.

'Yeh,' she said, breezily, 'Why not? I'd like to get to know you.'

Her Irish drawl sent my heart into overdrive, but I kept it in check.

'Great,' I replied, eagerly, 'I mean, that's good. Great. Cool.' I tried to tone it down. 'Can I have your number?'

I passed her my phone, and she saved her digits in my phonebook, under 'Siobhan :)'. I liked the use of the smiley face. It gave me hope. She must know I'm a lesbian; it's obvious just from looking at me. Stereotypes exist for a reason. Often, being a 'stereotypical lesbian' is helpful to me. It helps me to get noticed and to receive attention from girls. They're less shy in approaching me in a flirty way because of how I look. Where's the problem with that?

'I'll text you later,' I say, 'And yes, I'm okay. I get panic attacks, but nothing too debilitating. I'll be okay in a moment or two.'

With that she walked away, throwing a glance back over her shoulder at me. She looked very smart, much smarter than I did, in her cute white blouse and fitted trousers. I wanted her even then.

'Speak soon,' I hollered after her. She smiled again, which I could see even once her head had turned back to face forward, as the crease of her smile climbed the right side of her face slightly. She smiled mostly with the right of her face, which I found endearing, as it left small, dimple-like imprints on her cheek.

I'd text her tonight, I thought. I'll text her as soon as I leave work.

Brixton

September 1998

By September 1998, Kyle and I were both at the local secondary school, and Kyle had managed to ingratiate both of us into our new surroundings by declaring that our natural mum was a successful, but now underground, prostitute. 'Underground' potentially in the quite literal sense, as we had heard neither pop nor squeak from her in several years — since the morning of 15th March 1993, in fact — and so figured that she could well be dead. There was simply no way to know either way.

Being the children of a prostitute made us cool and respected. I'm not quite sure why, but it did. I had been smoking since I started at the school, Kyle had smoked even before that. Simone pretended not to know. We were popular with the other children at the school, possibly even slightly feared, as though we were naturally hard, born hard, because Mum was a slapper. 'Slapper'. What a terrible word.

Some of the meaner kids would sometimes come up to either Kyle or I and suggest that they'd seen Mum mainlining heroin on some alley floor, or else eating out of a dumpster, giving their dad a blowie, or wait for it, dead. Yes, they thought they'd seen her 'dead'. Never mind that they'd never met her or knew what she looked like; that's right, they'd seen her dead. The 'dead mum' rumours soon stopped once Kyle hit one of the ringleaders though, and Kyle soon gained a reputation as the type of kid who sorted things out with 'solid action'. In spite of this, and Kyle's definitive actions to repel any such mean-spirited comments from other kids, it was hard to hear their suggestions, as we really didn't know what had happened to Mum, and whether or not she was still alive.

Kyle was now, thankfully, back under the same roof as me, due to Simone fucking the man of the married Christian couple who were looking after him. No, really. They had a full-blown affair. We know all of the intimate, dirty little details. All of them, including where it all happened and what they did each time. Kids find out everything. Simone knows we know, which makes it all the funnier. It all came out back in summer '96, long before I was due to start at the secondary school, and Simone had to leave the church immediately. Kyle moved back in with us in July/August 1996, having been away from us for nearly a year. Naturally, the man was forgiven, and they are still together, this married couple. Naturally!

The church elite tried to suppress the rumours and the inevitable fallout, but gossips are everywhere, even in the house of God. Sometimes, especially in the house of God. The fact that Simone was still technically married — something the church elders of course knew — made it all the worse.

It was sad for Simone. She was part of a choir at the church and everything, plus her little circle of Christian friends. I could sympathise. Kyle was a fraction more hardened at this point, however he did stop setting fire to things. I reasoned with him, and together we realised that Simone had lost a lot so we would start trying to be a bit nicer to her. I was nicer to her than Kyle anyway, just tended to keep things from her and smoke against her will, but now we both strove to be a touch nicer to her. Looking back, though we didn't realise it at the time, I think the reason we both sympathised with Simone over 'affair-gate' was due to our own understanding of our real mum's life, who was certainly no saint when it came to her dealings with the opposite sex.

We didn't move house (Simone claimed she couldn't afford to — how come, Simone? Thought that man in Norway had lots of money?), but Simone did have to start up at a new church. We thought her experience might have made her less Christian, more child-friendly, but instead she was even more hardcore than ever, and had taken to reading the Bible aloud at dinner. We just ignored her when she did this.

I was starting to worry about how the future might look due to my preferences. I was feeling very strongly towards other girls. I had no doubt in my mind as to how Simone would receive this information — badly — so I kept it from her. I even kept it from Kyle for a long time. I would need to bide my time, I reasoned with myself, see how the feelings develop. Boy, did they develop.

I made a new friend at school, Laura. Laura was quite straightlaced compared to me, and was in many ways a good influence. Even Simone liked her, which was saying something. Simone also got on with her mother, Anne, who was a cleaner in the local doctor's surgery, so Simone would let me invite Laura over for dinner sometimes at our house. It was a kind gesture, and the first friend any of us children had been able to have in the house who wasn't a Christian friend decided for us by Simone.

I'd started to contemplate whether it might be worth telling Laura about my feelings. I didn't have them towards her, but maybe she would understand that I had them generally. I decided telling Kyle right now might not be the best thing, as he was struggling with a lot of his own emotions, however maybe I could tell Laura?

I decided that by thirteen I would do it. Thirteen came and went, then I was fast approaching fourteen and my SATs year. Would I ever find the chance to be honest about who I was? Was this who I was? I was becoming increasingly restless and in need of some kind of distraction from my confused headspace.

In April 1999 there was a nail bomb attack near Brixton market. It was followed by two subsequent, similar attacks in other London districts. We'd always been allowed to walk home from secondary school just the pair of us, Kyle and I, but now Simone started picking us up in her car, which was a tad embarrassing. Once the killer's motives started to become clearer, Simone became even more worried about Elsa and Darone, who were still both at the primary school, and wondered aloud if it was even safe to send them to school full stop. Brixton was alive with panic, confusion and fear, and Simone cried at length for a few days before the residents in the area, and Simone, gradually settled back into a normal routine.

Kyle continued to get into trouble, and started smoking pot, again, without Simone's permission/supposed knowledge. I too began drinking and occasionally smoked weed, too, though by no means as often as Kyle did. Simone must have smelt the cigarettes and pot, but said nothing. Kyle meanwhile had a string of girlfriends, even from an early age, which alarmed Simone, who worried what they were up to (not that she could talk after affair-gate), and the perhaps more obvious concerns of teenage pregnancy. Everyone, including Kyle, knew that Kyle couldn't look after himself, let alone a baby.

One Tuesday afternoon, while I was in Year 9, I came home from school and Simone wanted to have 'a chat'. She wasn't at any kind of meeting that evening, which was unusual, as she was a busy bee and usually came home at around five p.m. most evenings, having been to some kind of social event. Simone wanted to know my plans for the future. I had long stopped having the additional tutoring that Simone had arranged for me (due to my sustained protestations at the time) and hadn't expressed any interests of note in some time. I kept away from Simone when at home and tried to go out as much as possible. Now that I was a little older, Simone would let me out until teatime, and I often hung around with a slightly older group of girls, drinking in the park. Laura was not among this crowd, and I was seeing less of her.

'Not a lot,' I replied, honestly, 'I haven't really thought about it much.'

Simone's face grew cold. 'You must have some kind of plan,' she countered, 'You have always been so, so bright.'

She looked disappointed. For all her faults, Simone did seem to care about Kyle and I and I know she wanted us both to want for more. I took a moment to think, sincerely, about what I wanted.

'I want a factory job,' I said, 'Something manual so I can keep active. A nice partner, and a stable home.'

She smiled sadly. I think she knew this was probably the truth, and she wouldn't get much else out of me. She was right to think that.

* * *

Christmas 1999 came and went, along with the new millennium, to little fanfare. It was neither a harmonious nor an overly disruptive time; it was just a time, with little for me to recall in great detail. Kyle and I had started to grow slightly closer to Elsa and Darone, though they still barely spoke, even as they were nearing double digits, which was rather odd. We still knew very little about their background.

Simone's mother had come to us for Christmas '99; a quiet and stoic lady, she was a calming presence for growing children such as us. Not much company, and yet somehow all the company that was ever needed to diffuse any tensions. She said little, and yet achieved much just through being there and being kind enough of spirit that none of us ever wished to dismay or upset her. In her silence she held the power of us never knowing what she really thought of us, and certainly none of us wanted to dampen whatever thoughts they were. Simone knew we found her mother's presence comforting and so her mother was often with us at Christmastime. Kyle and I had never known any of our grandparents, so Simone's gentle mother was a welcome guest.

Simone decided that she would take us all to Camborne in Cornwall in summer of 2000. It was our first holiday as a group. Before then, Simone had claimed she couldn't afford to take us away, and the only time I'd been away with her was individually, back in year 8, when she took me to a piano recital in Stratford and we stayed in a Travelodge as a treat. We'd actually had a really nice time together, though no major heart-to-hearts as I hadn't wanted that kind of relationship with her, and still didn't.

I remember Simone packing up her dirty Gainesboro grey car out on the leafy suburban street. She had a vintage SUV that would have been quite a collectible had she bothered to take care of it; instead, it was tatty and the exhaust discharged a worryingly black smog every time she kickstarted the engine. Simone hauled our many holiday bags out to the car as we watched, chewing gum.

There weren't half as many animals weaving in and out of our legs on Simone's street, as there had been at Mum's: Simone was probably the main pet-owner on our street, with her three cats. Our neighbours on Simone's street didn't talk much, and seemed to live quite solitary lives. One or two of them owned a dog they took for walks. One of Simone's cats had died a couple of years ago, but she'd soon found a replacement, adamant as she was on having three cats. The new addition wasn't ginger like the others but bright white with a ginger cheek. Very cute but seemed bad-natured and would growl at us kids a lot.

On the drive down to Camborne, Simone sang a lot in her pretty, soprano voice. I realised on this drive how pretty she was herself, with her strawberry blonde hair and ashen complexion, curls spilling over the steering wheel. She had light auburn eyes and an endearing smattering of freckles on both cheeks. Occasionally she'd turn round to ask us how we were, shouting slightly over the country music she blasted out on the car radio. It was a lovely drive down, and I remember it well; Simone chose to take the low road through Dorset, and we enjoyed some beautiful views all the way down. Camborne was where she had holidayed as a child with her parents, she told us. She had been an only child, and it had sometimes been lonely. How great, she deducted aloud to us, that we could all hang out as a little quartet? We grimaced at the thought and the cringey attempt at forced intimacy.

Although there hadn't been much trouble lately of note, Kyle was still smoking pot, increasingly so as he grew older, and had gotten in with a bad crowd in Streatham. I had also had a couple of scrapes with the law within the year prior to our Camborne trip and Simone had once or twice been visited by the local bobbies because I had been seen regularly drinking in the park. Thankfully she didn't come down on Kyle and I too hard, or pay much heed, not even when I punched a boy in the year below for starting on Kyle. I should stress that it was the only time I ever punched anyone. I think Simone had given up trying to police Kyle, and I and had come to the realisation that it was probably best just to let us figure our own ways out.

The Camborne trip was a high point in our time with Simone and was to be the last high point for a while. During the trip we had little entertainment (Simone would not take us quad biking at the nearby quad biking centre, despite Kyle's pleads), and so made do with the endless joy of our old safe bet when it came to playtime fun: hide-and-seek with Elsa and Darone, without actually searching for them. We'd done this for hours as younger kids, and Elsa and Darone had never refused to play, despite their awareness that we would not come looking for them. I think they were fairly scared/intimidated by both of us. Simone drank brandy in the quaint cottage living room and pretended not to know what was going on. Ignorance was increasingly becoming her failsafe way of dealing with Kyle and I. Ignorance, brandy and singing. When she wasn't singing, she would sit for hours, staring ahead, alone with her thoughts.

As Kyle and I pretended to be counting and 'looking for Elsa and Darone', we concocted a plan for when we got back to London: we would try to find Mum. We were older now and could figure out where she lived. It was easy enough and Brixton wasn't that big, not really. We would definitely find her. It was a safe bet, like the pleasure of hide-and-seek with Elsa and Darone. It was failsafe, like ignorance and brandy.

Hull

March 2020

My troubling dreams intensified and increased in number, and it seemed as though we were due to go into some kind of 'national lockdown' soon, as other countries around the world and particularly in Europe were doing this, so I arranged an emergency counselling session with Lara. I wanted to be sure I could see her in person before it wasn't allowed anymore. I would of course use Skype or Zoom to have sessions with her when needed, but I would prefer to see her in the flesh in the first instance. It seemed a lot more personal and easier for me to open up if I could physically be with her in the same room.

She wanted me to regress back to childhood memories, which I did, but it was very hard. I told her about the portrait of the white deer I had, how some evenings I would get mildly tipsy and stare at it for hours on end. I told her about how Darone was starting to open up to me about all kinds of things, and how sometimes I didn't really want him to. He had started getting very drunk in the evenings after work and telling me about how his dad had abused him when he was little, but the stories weren't overly coherent to follow, and he always changed the subject when it got too deep, so it was hard to process his stories properly or know how best to respond. I told Lara what I had told Darone:

that I'm here to talk to him if he wants to talk to me when sober but the drunk stories were getting too much. I was dealing with enough stuff of my own.

Otherwise, it was still nice to have Darone around and I didn't begrudge his presence. He was helpful with Baxter, feeding and walking him when I wasn't around. But still, eventually he would need to move on. It had been a month, and I only really wanted him for two months, max. At some point he would need to move on, by force or by nature.

'He doesn't seem keen to move on this time,' I offloaded to Lara, worriedly, 'I'm scared he'll be here for a while.'

'You have enough of your own stuff going on,' Lara said, affirming and supporting my own doubts and future decisions. 'You shouldn't have to deal with his as well.' She paused, then chose to move to a lighter subject, 'How's it going with Siobhan?'

What I liked about Lara is that she remembered everyone's name. Everyone in my life, she remembered their names, their history, their relationship to me. In retrospect I realise that's how she earns her keep, but of course in the moment it makes you feel special. That's the whole point, though, isn't it? She wants me to feel special when speaking to her so that I continue to use her services. It's all money, isn't it? It's all about money. Money does everything, opens every door. Money and power. I didn't really have either, nor did I have a penis. Another thing which can help you to acquire money and power. What are my odds in life, I wonder?

'Good,' I said, honestly. 'I'm seeing her later.'

In fact, I'd seen a fair bit of Siobhan recently. We'd tried to make the most of this time, knowing that we were almost certain to go into some kind of lockdown soon. Siobhan would meet me in Princess Park on weekends and we'd walk Baxter around it a few laps. We did it some evenings as well. The weather was generally quite nice at the moment, and it was good to get to know her. She lived only a few streets away on Beresford Avenue, so it was convenient for both of us. She was living with her sister, she told me. Her sister studied at the university and Siobhan had moved over with her for a change of scenery.

'I had an ex in Ireland,' she'd told me. 'It ended badly. He wasn't a very nice person. It's good to be away from all of that.'

I wasn't getting an overly romantic vibe from Siobhan, sadly, but it was good to spend time with her. We both had a need for the friendship.

Lara asked if I had thought about downloading Tinder or some other kind of dating platform, trying to meet someone over that. To be perfectly honest, I was feeling quite depressed and not up to meeting girls at the moment. Regular walks with Siobhan were about all I could stretch to. I told Lara this and she said, no worries. That I should do things in my own time. That I should do things when I feel ready to. But time felt like it was running out. Time felt like it was not on my side.

* * *

That evening, I met Siobhan in Princess Park, in our usual spot. I wanted to understand her angle a bit more, considering mine, and know for sure whether or not I was wasting my time. Similarly, though, Siobhan was a colleague, so I didn't want to spook her or make her feel uncomfortable, as this could get back to work. Somewhere there was a middle ground I hoped we could both venture to.

'You know I'm a lesbian, right?' I put it out there, bold as brass. I hadn't intended to be quite so forthright, but I wanted to gauge her reaction, see if we were on the same page. I didn't know Siobhan's exact age, but she looked around early thirties, not too different from my own age.

'Yes,' she smiled, 'I think everyone knows that.'

I found that mildly reassuring, to think that she already knew. Part of me thought, why are you here? Why are you seeing me so often if not to see where this goes?

The spring sun shone down on us both and the air was fresh and crisp as she said, 'I'm bisexual.'

That was it, left in the mix. Left to hang in the clear, March sky. Left to sit with the pigeons, squatting on the branches of the tall fir trees, soon to dive down and scavenge for discarded food and crumbs among the grassland. I was one of those pigeons: desperate for a little bit more from Siobhan, like a touch, or a look of love, or something else I could cling to in hope.

Without meaning to, I let out a sigh. Siobhan chuckled in response, probably unsure how else to address my obvious despondency at her revelation. Steph had been bisexual, and where had that got me? Dumped, is where it had got me. Dumped and substituted by a man. What did he have that I didn't? I still couldn't understand that whole situation. What was so wrong with me? Why am I not the one Steph is with now? Where is she now? What is she doing?

I stopped, pulled Baxter closer to me on his lead. I closed my eyes, took deep breaths. Poor Siobhan must've been struggling to understand what was going on. Eventually, I broke the silence, if just to alleviate Siobhan of the burden of it.

'My ex was bisexual,' I said, still looking down to the ground, 'I have a bad experience of that.'

Siobhan smiled coyly, as if assuming I was hinting at us, me and her, and what that might involve. I had crossed an unspoken line here, drawn in the sand: the prospect of Siobhan and I. Both of us knew it, then, in that moment, what this was. This was me getting to know Siobhan. This was Siobhan getting to know me. I burned with passion for someone, a nice lady. But I just as quickly burned with a desire to leave things well alone if I couldn't be sure that they were good for me. I was getting older, wiser. I had done things by now, lived through them, loved and been hurt so many times. I wasn't ready to take any chances, not really. I was really, really hurting, still, after all this time.

'I just fall in love with the person,' Siobhan consoled, 'Not what's in their pants. I'm sorry you had a bad experience with your ex.'

She reached over to brush my arm and committed to the action. It was gentle but it spoke a thousand words. I shuddered at her touch. It was getting later now, and the air was fast getting colder. A breeze whipped past us as she touched me, and both brought on the goosebumps: her touch and the slight wind.

'I think I'm too far gone,' I said, sadly, looking into Baxter's large, chocolate eyes, 'I don't know if I'm ever going to meet anyone, and when I do, maybe I won't be able to open myself up to love anymore.'

Siobhan moved closer to me, slowly. She put a small, cold hand to my face, stroked the cheek. I looked into her big, green eyes, and leant in to kiss her. It was a small, unimposing kiss — more of a peck, if anything — under the boughs of a great oak tree.

'I think you'll be okay,' she said after, looking at me still. She'd worn a long green overcoat and black boots, and I liked her understated make-up, which only really consisted of eyeliner and a little foundation. 'I've met people more messed up than you.'

'Me too,' I replied, honestly. We walked slowly up the grass verge to my street. 'Can I see you tomorrow?'

Siobhan said she wasn't around tomorrow, had to take her sister to a doctor's appointment.

'I'll text you,' she said, walking away. She turned round to smile and to wave. I worried she was getting cold feet, that she regretted the kiss. Maybe she regretted ever meeting me outside of work. Left with my anxious mind, I pulled Baxter gently by the lead and ambled back to my house.

Brixton

October 2000

It was October 2000, the same year as our summer Camborne trip. Simone had met a new fancy man at her choir. We were pleased for her; she hadn't really dated anyone in the whole time we'd known her, and she'd not even spoken about men or even her estranged Norway-based husband since affair-gate. We hoped romance might soften her a bit, make her more approachable and friendly. She used to go for dinner with this man, leaving me in charge as the eldest. I'd open her brandy cupboard and pour Kyle and I a glass. We hated the taste, but it made us feel like adults. Elsa and Darone naturally did not get a look in.

One of the evenings we were put in charge of the younger children, Kyle and I informed them that we would be off shortly, in search of our real mum. Elsa and Darone, true to form, said nothing by way of reply. We told them that if Simone came home early, they were to tell her that we'd nipped out for some baked beans and bread from Mr Khatri's corner shop at the end of the road. We didn't anticipate being out for very long: we were just going to take a look at Mum's place then come home — the same amount of time we'd usually spend in Mr Khatri's. It was a plausible story: we were often in the kindly man's store, buying things we technically weren't old enough to buy. He was a very friendly man considering that only a few years ago he had caught Kyle stealing lighters from him, although it was also well-known at that time (the time of lighter-gate) that Kyle and I had had a 'troubled' upbringing (Simone confided a lot to her Christian friends who thus told everyone else in the locale; 'troubled' in inverted commas because it's quite a patronising and reductive way to describe a child's early life, isn't it, when really we didn't have bad memories of Mum or of our early childhood, hence why we were going to try to find her. 'Troubled' because that's how adults would describe Kyle's and my early life, not how we'd necessarily describe it ourselves), so Mr Khatri was likely inclined towards compassion and forgiveness towards Kyle's younger misdemeanours. Indeed, he'd never really chastised Kyle over lighter-gate at all, and now seemed happy to see us in his store, regularly asking us how we were and how Simone was.

For now, though, we were en route to Mum's, and decided to take the 72 bus. We knew that once we saw the chippy on the corner, to press the bell. The bus would take us slightly past Mum's road, and then we'd need to retrace our steps for a hundred yards or so to Temple Close. We didn't think in 'yards' back then, of course, but that's by the by. Suffice to say that we knew it wasn't too far from the bus stop.

The journey went smoothly enough with no hiccups. The sky outside the bus window was grey and threatened rain that never came. It seemed to grow darker the closer we got to Mum's, but perhaps that was just our own sense of foreboding. I felt inclined to grab Kyle's hand on the way down by way of reassurance, but neither of us would have appreciated that kind of gesture anymore, as we were both cool now and therefore not willing to be seen holding hands with each other. In front of us on the bus sat a very smelly man who mumbled nonentities for most of the journey and stank of cheap beer.

The stop came soon enough, and we alighted. Turning onto Mum's street was a bit of a shock: no animals roamed the streets like they used to, but the crisp and chocolate packets and wrappers still swirled and danced above the smoky road. Time seemed to stand still, the air seemed to stop letting us breathe as inhaling and exhaling became a sudden chore, something we needed to think about. Empty bottles cradled themselves by the roadside gutters, the pavements sunk in on themselves. The shoddy-looking bungalows on the right-hand side of the cul-de-sac seemed to curve into the floor, eyes seemed to secretly watch behind closed blinds. The bins still overflowed; the rats still found their dinner.

This was a mistake.

We were here, though, and desperate for answers. We sidled slowly up to the end of the road, where Mum's apartment building stood. The crosswire fence next to us no longer housed a barking dog; we squinted for a familiar face, perhaps Mrs Crabby, but could find no knowing eyes. We looked up to the middle flat, where Mum would be. There was nothing for a long time, and still we continued to stare, hoping we might see something. Suddenly, a woman moved across the front room. We knew it was a woman because of the shape of her right arm. We couldn't catch her hair colour or anything else, so we decided to try ringing the doorbell. In normal times that would have been a terrible idea, but we were chomping at the bit to know how Mum was. Social hadn't bothered with us in years (almost as soon as Simone confirmed she would keep us, they stopped caring how we were) and Simone didn't ask us much about Mum or indeed about anything. This was our time, our right to know what had happened to her.

I was selected to press the bell, as the older sibling and also because I always wanted to protect Kyle. Perhaps it was the natural role I took on once we were taken from Mum. I had always felt part sister and part mother to Kyle.

We tentatively climbed the metal stairwell, its white paint chipped and bleeding away. The building definitely looked shabbier than we remembered, and we were feeling very apprehensive about what we were doing, but it also felt like a rite of passage, something we couldn't not do. When we got to Mum's landing, a coarse, metal frame separating us from her front door, we hesitated.

'I'm not sure—' I turned to Kyle, 'What if she doesn't want us back?'

Kyle looked frenzied, his eyes wild with confusion. I hadn't turned round on the stairwell so I hadn't seen his expression, but now it dawned on me. He was even more miserable and despairing than me. He needed me to do this. I needed to be the mum neither of us had anymore.

I swallowed and leant forward. I took an extra, shallow step to reach the door. The doorbell had long been removed, incomplete wires hanging dangerously from where it once lived, as though it had been ripped out. I knocked, very gently, three times.

There was a long pause that felt like forever, and then several thuds inside, like someone large was approaching the door, and then he appeared, having yanked open the door with great ease, a huge, burly man with tattoos on his face and arms. He was at least six foot and crowded the doorway, muscles bulging under a black tank top. Veins seemed to pulsate from his temples. He did not look happy.

Before we could explain, and we were about to, a sliver of a woman scurried up next to him, with bouncy brown hair and large breasts that sat at odds with her otherwise very petite frame. Attractive, but certainly not my mum.

'Who are these little ones?' she asked, in a thick Essex accent, her breasts trying to squeeze a space into the congested doorway as she leaned into us.

'I — er—' I choked.

Unlike the curious woman, the man was not pleased to see us, and his eyes flamed large and angry. 'You better go,' he said, in no uncertain terms, 'Before this gets nasty.'

* * *

Not finding Mum deflated me (and made for an unhappy fifteenth birthday in late 2000), but it broke Kyle. Not satisfied with weed to numb his depression, by Christmas 2000 his 'friends' had introduced him to cocaine. Ah, cocaine. The party drug. The drug we can only assume had been Mum's dabble of choice. The drug that was about to tear our lives apart.

Things had been going well between Simone and her fancy man, and we met him a few times. Kyle, now in the throes of a multitude of addictions, was bad company during the festive season into 2001, and did not give a good first impression to 'Greg', as we would come to know Simone's new man. Thankfully we did not have to live through the horror of Greg moving in (Simone was determined to do things the proper, Christian way since the catastrophe of affair-gate, so no 'living in sin') however we did have to listen to his deconstructions of us and his character analyses of our inner workings. With the cacophony of shit going on inside of Kyle, Greg is lucky he didn't end up murdered.

It was good to see Simone slightly happier, though, and I sensed that she was glad of someone else around who she could voice her pains to. I think we disappointed her. I was approaching my final year of school and had made it clear that I wasn't interested in doing any A levels. Kyle's cocaine addiction was about to rip a hole in our makeshift family. Simone probably needed Greg.

Summer 2001, just before I turned sixteen and Kyle was still only fifteen, would put us both through the biggest hell yet.

Hull

June 2020

It was June 2020, and I woke up from the most vivid dream: Kyle and I running through clean, green fields behind the back of a disused industrial park, the fresh summer air whipping about our faces. I turned round to find Mum but — Mum? Mum? I woke up with my hands gripping the bed sheets in tight fists.

We'd been in a national lockdown for just over two months when an American man was killed by a police officer kneeling on his neck. The victim had been a black man and the videos had shocked the Western world. Darone, naturally, was incensed by the events and wanted to take part in the 'Black Lives Matter' protests happening across the country. I, meanwhile, was hoping for a way to get Darone out of my house. Somewhere, there was a compromise in this situation.

'You should go,' I said, without hesitation, when Darone suggested attending a London rally in early June 2020. 'This is important to you. Coronavirus won't kill me or you. Hell, I'm still going into work and there are loads of people there. Go for it. Have fun. Make it worthwhile.'

Darone could smell a rat. 'Sick of me already?' he ventured.

I sighed. There was no easy way to address this issue, and he'd been living with me now for the best part of four months.

'This is my home,' I said, amicably. I wanted to reach common ground with Darone, but I also wanted my space back as soon as possible. 'I don't want you as a house guest forever, no. But you must know that already. In fact, I think I've done remarkably well to tolerate having a house guest for this long.'

Darone looked dejected rather than angry. I was relieved; I had worried that he would instead be angry. I moved to hug him.

'You're family,' I said genially. 'We look out for each other. But I want my own home. No, I don't want you here forever.'

We agreed that Darone would attend the London rally, then go back to Simone and Greg's for a bit, possibly Elsa's. Greg wasn't horrible to Darone, and Darone had a home with them. It was more when Darone first came out that Greg had been difficult with him. They were slightly better now. I think everyone hoped that Darone would eventually find his feet somewhere, but some people take longer than others to find their calling in life. I know that as well as anyone. Hell, I'm still looking myself.

'Do you want to come to the rally too?' Darone asked hopefully. I shook my head, almost on impulse.

'I respect the cause,' I replied honestly, 'But it doesn't mean a lot to me personally. You should go, though. Definitely.'

Darone left on good terms, and we agreed he could visit again soon. On his way out, he asked, 'That lady, Siobhan. She seems nice. Is anything happening there?'

'I don't know,' I replied, 'I really don't. Now go on, you've got a train to catch.'

East Yorkshire rail services were rarely on time, but Darone needn't know that. I wanted time alone with my thoughts and my dog.

* * *

The day that Darone left, Siobhan came over the same evening. She'd visited before for dinner, but this time she came over to stay the night. We weren't a couple or anything, but a couple of the male managers from work had caught wind of our budding romance and liked to poke fun, nonetheless. I was a typical 'butch-looking' lesbian and Siobhan was very femme, so I'm sure they were able to make plenty of jokes at our expense. Siobhan let slip that they had made a couple of comments to her. I was fairly enraged by this and imagined she could see my temperature rising when she had said, 'Don't worry, Chris. I can handle it. Thanks though,' before lightly dusting my ear with the fingertips of her right hand.

Tonight, when she came over, I had ready a chilli tomato and king prawn pasta dish. I'd love to say it was fully made from scratch, but it wasn't. We weren't technically allowed to visit each other's house due to the coronavirus pandemic, but neither Siobhan or I overly cared for the rules, and we were mixing with more people at our workplace, plus neither of us had regular or indeed any contact with elderly people, so meeting up felt justified. It was either that or both of us went mad. I know which option I preferred. Whatever possible drawbacks you could ever pose to me, my answer would always be that I wanted to see Siobhan. She was so beautiful and so likeable. It was a no-brainer.

Sometimes I worried she only met up with me because she was lonely. She and her sister had only been in England for a matter of months, and so maybe she just wanted the company and companionship? Maybe she didn't care for me much at all? I suppressed the thought whenever it came up.

'How did your sister's exam go?' I asked Siobhan, carefully removing her green coat to reveal a lovely, pink summer dress underneath. She looked a vision, with scant make-up and gently coiffed hair. I hung up her coat on the wall rack before she tossed her tussled, long hair over her shoulder in a ladylike way and followed me through to the kitchen.

'Yeh, good,' she said, 'Though I'm not sure she prepared for it as well as she should have done.'

Siobhan's sister, Chloe, studied zoology at the university. From what I understood, the university was good for animal studies, particularly if you wished to specialise in marine biology. Most of it went over my head, but Siobhan could hold her own with a lot of subjects. She reckoned I could, too, if I put my mind to it. Said I was probably a good deal brighter than I gave myself credit for. I usually responded that I wasn't much interested in higher or lofty things, and Siobhan would leave it at that.

I had used the few hours in-between Darone leaving and Siobhan arriving to tidy up, and the house looked much better. I had plenty of space; like I said before, money goes quite far in Hull. You can get quite a nice place for not a lot of buck, here. Siobhan sat down at my small, MDF dining room table as I poured her a glass of zinfandel white wine. She liked white wine, and it paired well with prawns.

We had a nice meal and sat down to watch TV together. Siobhan was happy to watch the trash I did, but occasionally wanted to watch a documentary. Usually a historical documentary. She also liked period dramas, like *Pride and Prejudice*. I didn't like period dramas much, but I let her watch them from time-to-time and would just sit on my phone, playing games or texting.

We sat drinking wine and watching *Hollyoaks* when Siobhan asked how my dreams had been lately. I told her that I'd been struggling with them still. I didn't go into the specifics: my dreams usually involved finding out Mum was dead, then seeing a pool of blood on the floor, with her bright, red hair fanned out and trailing in the blood. Siobhan didn't need to know the finer details.

'You should go to your GP,' she said, then corrected herself, 'Well, call them.' No one is allowed to visit their doctor in the current, coronavirus climate. 'They might be able to prescribe you something.'

I wasn't sure about that. I was pretty anti-medication and wary of most prescriptions.

I shrugged, 'I'm sure they'll go away in time.'

Siobhan frowned. She still didn't know a great deal about my past yet and I didn't want to disclose everything to her. There was still a lot of reservation in me. I was holding back more than she was.

Around ten p.m., we made our way up to my bedroom. It was a tidy room, with a pale blue carpet and cream walls. I had painted some rooms, but not in here. I had old, oak furniture with plenty of rustic charm, including a giant, 1920s wardrobe in dark mahogany. Most of them charity shop buys. Charity shops arrange delivery services now, so you can buy big furniture items and not worry about how to cart them home; they'd bring a van round later in the week. The old furniture wouldn't have been to my taste when I was younger, as I would probably have found it a bit creepy looking, but now I was older I found the furniture quaint and cute in its own way. I also had a small TV in the corner of the room, and plenty of room. As I mentioned before, it was the master bedroom, so it was a decent-sized room. Hull had been badly bombed in the blitz of 1941, but my street hadn't suffered any casualties. The house had stood proud since 1935.

When it came to it, I wasn't up to sex. Siobhan looked so lovely, and I ached to touch her and to move inside her, but I ached more from everything else. Mostly, I ached just to be near to her. I ached just to hug and kiss, and to lie next to her as she slept. Those were the main things I wanted to do.

I sat on the end of the bed, and she closed the door gently behind me. She took her own dress off and placed it on the floor. She removed one peach bra strap, then another. She sat on top of me, and I felt the warmth of her through her knickers. I was burning to feel the wetness of her pussy, could feel it throbbing through her underwear. She kissed my neck seductively and stroked the top of my back, then my hair. It was taking all of me not to ravish her then and there, not to throw her onto her back on the bed and finger her like crazy. I wanted to. I so wanted to. We kissed deep and long for some time, before she realised I wasn't going to make love to her.

'What's wrong?' she whispered in my ear. Even just her whispering made me tingle with delight.

'I-just,' I was still kissing her while I was speaking, 'I just don't think I'm ready yet.'

She stopped kissing me, let go of my hair. She pushed away from me, moved over to the opposite side of the bed.

'Okay,' she said, then again after a moment or two, 'Okay.'

'There's more going on than I've told you,' I said, honestly. 'I just need a bit more time.' Noticing the sadness in her eyes I added, 'I want you. I really, really want you but,' I fought for the words. I wanted to give her the right words, down to every last letter, not just the words that were okay. I wanted to give her the very best words. 'I've been through a lot. Loads more than I've even told you about yet. I'm hurting so, so much. I've given of myself so much and I just want to be sure of something before giving again. I really, really want you. I've really, really enjoyed everything about us, everything about getting to know you. But you don't know the full picture yet. There's so much more about me that I need to show you before I'm physical with you. Please understand. I'm sorry if you feel led on. You aren't being. I couldn't be more attracted to you. I just need time.'

It was the absolute truth. I'm not sure I could've wanted anyone any more than I wanted Siobhan right now.

'I've been physical with a lot of girls. More than I should have been, really. Most of the time with them it was just about burying grief. About not dealing with the core issues. It was fun but it was masking something deeper and stronger. I had so much I should've been working through when instead I just went out and slept with random girls. That wasn't right. I should've been working through my demons. I don't want you to be a random girl. I want you to be more than that. So, I'm holding off on sleeping with you. I'm sorry if you thought that that's what would happen when you came round here to stay the night. To be honest, I thought it would happen, too. I thought it would happen until five minutes ago when I realised, I wasn't ready. Five minutes ago, I had a revelation. I was all guns blazing before that.'

'It's okay,' she said, moving closer to me, and kissing my cheek, 'No problem.'

'Look at you,' I said, looking into her watery eyes, 'Look at how beautiful you are. I'd be mad not to want you. I'm going to spend the whole night wanting you. I'm going to spend the whole night lying next to you and wishing I could be intimate with you.

Wishing I could taste you. Wishing I could love you. But I won't be able to do any of it, because it's not the right time. It will be one day, but it's not right now.'

Siobhan moved away again, looked around the room. 'Do you have any pyjamas I could wear?'

I went up to my navy chest of drawers and pulled out some cotton pyjamas from the top drawer. They were yellow and too long in both the arms and the leg for me, but they might be okay for Siobhan.

'Thanks,' she said, slipping them on. She lay back on the bed, gazed up at the ceiling.

I did the same.

'How much do you like me?' she asked, after a short while. I turned to face her, raised myself up on my elbows so that I was above her and leaned down to kiss her delicate, heart-shaped mouth.

'I like you more than you know,' I whispered, smoothing her fringe back so I could look deeper into her eyes. I noticed now how freckly both her cheeks were. 'More than I intended to and more than I was ready to. Enough to make it worth the ride.'

She smiled and nodded. 'I like you, too.'

She rolled over so I could spoon her from behind, and I kissed the crown of her head.

I flicked off the bedside light. After not too long, we fell asleep.

Just before falling asleep, though, Siobhan turned to me and said, 'Chris?'

'Mmm?' I mumbled, already half in the land of nod.

'Why so many Buddhas?'

Lesbians

And where do lesbians go from here?
Behind which door do they hide?
A linesman over the tannoy speaks,
'By thirty you've had your time.'
Do they turn to the bottle, love,
Or enter a long sleep?
Do they resolve to marry a man instead,
His food and clothes to keep?
Do they march in women's rallies when
The cause is all but faded?
Think they see their own in another, then,
Realise she's just as jaded?
Or do they smear their face in mud,
Sing a song that's past its prime?
You'll see me in your mind and say,
'I knew her at twenty-nine.'

Brixton

February 2001

Kyle had been self-harming for a while before the overdose, so I hadn't told him anything about my burgeoning sexuality. Little cuts had appeared all over his forearms, so I'd decided not to overwhelm him with any of my own issues. Simone must have noticed his cuts, too, but as ever turned to singing and alcohol to remedy her troubled mind. Greg must've also helped to ease the heavy burden of her having to look after Kyle and me. We'd stopped hiding her brandy — a malicious thing we did for fun when we were younger — so she was back on that in the evenings, and had taken up talking to herself. She was approaching forty now so was still a fairly young woman, albeit increasingly sad and ruminative. Her letters from her husband in Norway were becoming staggeringly less frequent.

Kyle and I had long stopped seeing the therapist Simone had arranged for us when we were younger, and besides, said therapist had — naturally — been a Christian therapist, so talk of lesbian sexuality would probably have been banned. There would have been right and wrong answers to give to the therapist, and even at nine years old I had been aware of this. Plus, I hadn't felt much sexuality-wise at nine, and by the time we stopped seeing the therapist, a year or so later, I still hadn't really developed strong sexual feeling of any kind. The therapist had overall been helpful though, certainly to me, and Simone had tactfully arranged for us to speak individually to a young female friend of hers rather than a stuffy old man, so that certainly helped. I did talk a lot about Mum during the sessions, and the therapist concluded that I displayed a healthy grieving technique, and that it was good that I felt able to talk about her so openly. When I had asked what she had meant — 'grieving' — the therapist had clarified that the move to Simone was permanent, so I would need to find constructive ways to deal with having left Mum. I understood this to be right, even at nine, but it didn't take away the pain, which stayed with me, year-on-year, gnawing in my side like a sharp summer thorn.

A teacher at school had wanted to speak with me, sensing that something was wrong. I didn't feel ready to disclose my sexuality, so just spoke to her about my life plans in general. I intended to move in with a friend, Janine, once I turned sixteen. Janine was slightly older than me at eighteen, and one of the friends I had become close to from drinking in the park together. She was effortlessly cool, with tight dreadlocks and several facial piercings. Janine had her own place above a bank with her boyfriend, and said I could move in with them, provided I got a job and paid my way. I relished the thought, and said yes at once, but hadn't yet told Simone. It didn't seem necessary to tell her yet, plus I figured she'd be delighted at the prospect of either Kyle or I leaving, considering that the bobby-visits were becoming less regular. I was now drunk in the parks most weekends, and Kyle was always in some kind of trouble.

The teacher nodded by way of reply, and said little else, the same sad look on her young face as Simone had displayed only a few months earlier when I had said much the same: that I didn't have much of a career plan, and wasn't really fussed whether I left school with a handful of GCSEs or not, never mind A-levels. She was my maths teacher and I had always been great at maths. But I could get a decent GCSE in it and still get a factory job, no problem.

News of Kyle's overdose came through on the mobile phone Simone had grudgingly bought for me when I turned thirteen ('only teenagers could have mobiles', she'd reasoned), and when I was walking home from school. Simone was frantic with worry, and her concern seeped through the mobile and into me. Kyle was currently in hospital, and his vital signs were good, but this could have a lasting effect on his kidneys. I wasn't too sure what or where the kidneys were, having never enjoyed or thrived at Biology, so I just took in what I could and arranged to meet Simone at the hospital.

Once there, we were silent for a while, waiting outside, before Simone asked me how my day had been, what I had been up to. It felt right to tell her my plans now, considering that she was probably grasping at straws for some kind of reassurance and truth. Some kind of clarity, some kind of definite answer.

'I spoke with my maths teacher, Mrs Underwood'.

Simone nodded: she knew all of my subject teachers and partly resented the suggestion that I'd needed to specify the name of my maths teacher when Simone already knew this detail.

'I'm going to move out at sixteen. I'm going to move in with my friend Janine and get a factory job.'

Simone looked crestfallen. I was surprised: I assumed that over the years Kyle and I had mostly caused her a multitude of pains, and that this would come as good news.

'I thought you'd be happy,' I went on, 'I thought Kyle and I caused you a lot of hurt. I thought you'd be glad of me gone; less to contend with.'

The unforgiving hospital strip lighting illuminated all of the nooks and crevices in Simone's quickly-aging face. She looked tired and worn out. She'd made an effort in her dress today, wearing a cerise cardigan, white pleated skirt and pretty gold pendant. Simone often wore bright colours that clashed, or clothes that were too baggy for her, so it was good to see her in something more fitting and complimentary. I'd noticed that since she'd been dating Greg, her general appearance and sense of style — bar the natural effects of an aging face — had significantly improved. Romance had helped her to blossom a bit.

The strip lighting also showed up the hospital floor, which was worryingly filthy. Hospitals often seem quite dirty in terms of their general amenities, don't you think? This hospital had a cheap linoleum floor, like so many other hospitals, and cracks in-between filled with dirt. Hospitals always feel like places to die, I think, not places to live.

'You've been so helpful over the years,' Simone said, generously, 'It's a shame you want to leave.'

I hadn't been very helpful, and I felt guilty now that Simone had put the onus back onto me. Want to leave? Why would I not?

I deliberated for a few moments over my reply to this. 'I think it would just be good for all of us,' I eventually surmised, 'To have a bit of space.' I paused, 'For me to have a bit of space.'

She thought about it for a moment, then nodded. She too could see the benefits of my having some space for a while.

'Please try to finish your GCSEs,' she insisted. 'For your own sake.'

I agreed to do this, though internally remained unsure I was committed to that deal.

Kyle ended up rallying and making a full recovery in a remarkably short space of time, including his kidneys, however the incident was to put an indelible stain on him and further strain his relationship with Simone. It transpired that the events leading up to the overdose had been less than perfect and Kyle's actions were less than angelic in the whole affair, so he was excluded from school for three months. That's a long time for a teenage boy to lose out on his education, and he and Simone would get into some very serious arguments. Simone would find items of hers missing, like expensive jewellery, which she assumed Kyle had taken to sell to a pawnbroker so that he could buy more drugs. It was all very sad. Simone never went to the police, bizarrely, hoping instead that she could keep it all within the family. The aftermath of affair-gate a few years ago and the shameful pain that had caused Simone still left a deep mark on her, and she was determined to never be embarrassed in such a way again. She would strive to keep matters within the four walls of her 1930s terraced house as much as she could, moving forwards.

With credit to her more recent church family, they were very supportive to Simone during this time, and suggested that Greg move in. Although it was technically against the advice and instruction of the Bible (that two unmarried people in a romantic relationship should live together), Simone's church family considered it best for Simone to have an authoritative male figure in the house who could better keep Kyle in check and, to a degree, protect Simone from Kyle's increasingly erratic behaviour. Inwardly (though I never acknowledged it outwardly to Kyle or to Simone or to anyone), I agreed this was probably the best thing for Simone, though it would lead to heightened tension in the house, no doubt, and I was evermore glad to be leaving the house in just a few months. It did cross my mind whether or not Simone's more recent church knew of her actual husband in Norway, however, a) Simone hadn't mentioned him in a long time, so potentially the separation had been finalised in some way; b) the church she belonged to at this time seemed a little more liberal (read: understanding) than her previous church, which had had a strange hierarchical system of elders and power struggles, etc (yes, really); and/or potentially, c) Simone hadn't actually told her current church about the man in Norway. To be perfectly honest, Simone hadn't really mentioned the man in Norway since 1995. It was a dirty secret she intended to keep secret at all costs, a dirty secret that was now no longer writing to her. I was mildly curious to know why he had stopped writing, but not curious enough to bother to ask.

By the time Greg moved in, and Kyle was back at school, I was only two months away from living with Janine and the plan continued to be a solid and definite one. I couldn't wait. Simone tried to make the transition of Greg moving in smooth, and organised lots of 'family activities' of an evening, such as playing Cluedo together etc, but it usually ended in arguments. Yes, even, and almost especially, Cluedo could end in ferocious arguments. We also had the odd daytrip out on the weekend, to the cinema or to a local park to feed some ducks, but that also usually ended badly. You couldn't force a dynamic that wasn't there, and Kyle and I kind of resented Greg, never mind the fact that we barely knew the guy, so we were more than happy to stir the pot and to stir up trouble. We enjoyed pranks, such as hiding his car keys for prolonged periods of time, or drinking Simone's alcohol, or winding Simone up so much that Greg flew into a blind rage at us. He wasn't our biggest fan at the best of times, and the home dynamic was frequently strained and volatile.

I was ready to go, and to do my own thing for a while. I had been for some time.

* * *

Kyle didn't react too warmly to my moving in with Janine and her boyfriend. When I say Kyle didn't react too warmly, I mean that he didn't speak to me for two whole months. For Kyle and me not to speak for two months is quite something, or certainly was at this time. We would go longer without speaking in the future, though this was yet to come.

Greg — a redhead with a thick Scottish accent and a strong personality — clashed immeasurably with Kyle. Drugs and drink were no longer permitted in any form, and, although Kyle and I had both done things like that outside of the house, such as round at a friend's place, Kyle was also forbidden to do them anywhere outside of the home. This didn't stop him, but he had to be careful what he smelt like when he came back to Simone's place after being with friends, as pot has a strong smell and Greg was no fool.

I was glad to be out of it all. I turned sixteen in November 2001 and had a great birthday. Things were going well at Janine's. I managed to get a job at weekends as a warehouse operative at a local fizzy soft drink factory and somehow managed not to fluff up my GCSE exams in late spring/early summer 2002. I say a local factory: the factory was actually several buses away and not in Brixton, however it was work and I could get a dayrider ticket, which saved me a lot of money on the bus fare. I worked 6–6 on both Saturday and Sunday each weekend, which was exhausting but which even at minimum wage meant I could pay Janine some rent money. Once summer hit and I had finished my exams, I increased my hours at the factory to four days a week. It was all looking positive. I even had my own room at Janine's, albeit a little small and with not much room for my things. I had never owned a huge number of things though so it wasn't a problem.

One weekday evening, while tipsy and slightly stoned, I decided to open up to Janine about my feelings. Her boyfriend Adam was out, and we were having a heart-to-heart. She was the first person I'd told about being lesbian, and thankfully she took it remarkably well.

'We'll sneak you into Cardinals,' she said excitedly. 'I've been there before with the girls and it's always a good night, gay or straight.'

'The Cardinal', or 'Cardinals' as it was locally known, was the leading gay bar in nearby Vauxhall. That and 'Gekko Bar'. Gekkos tended to be the pre-drink spot and Cardinals was the main event, as Gekkos didn't have a dancefloor, but Cardinals did. Cardinals also did themed nights, drag nights, karaoke, fancy dress, you name it, they did it. I was excited.

'Perhaps don't tell Adam, though,' Janine was keen to add on, 'We've been arguing recently, and I don't want him to get the wrong end of the stick. He can be...' She searched for the word, 'y'know...'

I didn't know, but I was grateful to be living with Janine and Adam and didn't want to rock the boat in any way, so just nodded amicably. I had noticed Janine and Adam arguing recently, but had chosen to turn a blind eye to all of it. It wasn't my business, and I was wise not to get involved. They were my hosts, so who am I to pry on their affairs?

I passed my GCSEs (not amazingly, but well enough to be in line for the sorts of jobs I was looking for) and was well into the throes of summer 2002. Things were looking up, and I would finally experience a gay bar and the LGBT world I had been burning to know. I couldn't wait to get started. I couldn't see the warning signs or red flags for the trees.

Hull

August 2020

On Siobhan's advice, I'd gone to my GP a month or two prior to August 2020, to discuss my nightmares and to see if the GP could prescribe me anything for them. I also mentioned my panic attacks, which were persistent but had been calming down recently. He prescribed me some anti-anxiety medication to take before bedtime, and I had been finding this medication useful.

The lockdown in England due to the coronavirus pandemic had been easing over summer, and I made plans for Simone to visit. I'd been having my therapy sessions with Lara over Zoom since the lockdown started, and she'd recommended Simone visit as soon as it was safe for her to do so, and more importantly permissible for her to do so. Lara felt that Simone and I would both benefit enormously from time spent together; she felt it would help us both to address and right any former wrongs or misunderstandings on the part of the other. I had nothing against Simone, really, and felt in agreement with Lara. What I differed in opinion with Lara on, though, was how soon Simone should visit. I was cavalier about coronavirus at the best of times: Simone could visit as soon as she wanted to.

Simone had been itching to visit for a while — hinting at it over and over in her letters to me — and it was only right that I let her come to stay and that we had some bonding time together. She was quite panicky about the drive up — 'won't the police pull me over?', she kept asking me — but we both agreed it was 'now or never' and that we had a lot of catching up to do and old wounds to heal. Simone was and always had been very 'new-agey' and didn't like social media technology, so everything was done through drawn-out snail mail or emotional phone calls. She did have an email account but barely used it. She was a queer thing, then as now. Hates technology but loves music. Dresses in clashing colours and shuns fashion sense. Refuses to carry around a bank card so instead travels with wads of cash in her purse. That's our Simone.

Before her visit, I arranged to meet Bobby, my friend from work, in a beer garden. We could go to pubs again now, but only if we sat in the beer garden, in a very small group of less than six people. Pubs had been closed until very recently, so Bobby and I were desperate to resume our beer garden communions. Not only this but as I knew him from work, he also knew Siobhan, and I wanted to get his opinion on everything. Two months after Siobhan and my fateful night together at my place and I still hadn't slept with her. The girl must be ready to blow with sexual desire.

I took a long drink from my pint of Fosters and waited for Bobby to ask about her.

When he didn't ask about her, I formulated the question myself.

'You know I've been meeting up with Siobhan outside of work?' I asked. Bobby rolled his eyes.

'Everyone knows you've been meeting up with Siobhan outside of work,' he grinned, slurping his Heineken, 'The owner of the whole factory probably knows.' He waited before asking the question he really wanted to know the answer to: 'Have you slept with each other yet?'

I paused. 'No,' I replied, 'That's the problem. I haven't, but I want to.'

Bobby couldn't suppress his laughter. 'You haven't but you want to? Who says that?'

I smiled. 'There's a lot going on for me,' I told him, truthfully, 'I'm not ready yet.'

Bobby nodded understandingly. 'I get it,' he said, smiling, 'Hopefully she will, too!' He drank a little more, then ventured, 'Siobhan is very attractive, and I'm sure she has other admirers at work. You should get to it before someone else does. She's thirty-three and good to go.'

Finally, I knew Siobhan's exact age. Not that it made much difference. We were close enough in age for it to be a well-matched relationship. Bobby momentarily worried me slightly with his suggestion that others at work fancy Siobhan — was he hinting that he himself might? — but I quickly rallied from that state-of-mind. Siobhan wanted me, sex or no sex. I would work through my shit and allow myself to be intimate with her in no time. Right?

* * *

'Not sure about the Buddhas,' Simone disclosed openly, having been in my house for the grand total of twenty minutes. She quickly added diplomatically, 'Love the white deer painting, though. Didn't you have that in your place with Steph?'

Simone was always quick off the ball. Quick to notice things, quick to register them, quick to cross-reference them, quick to remember select details. She was frighteningly observant,

91

frighteningly able to recall fine details in little time. Her latest car, a pink classic Mini with white stripes, sat comfortably on my drive next to my well-worn Ford Fiesta. Now she sat, herbal tea in hand, on my brown, PVC sofa. Despite being a cat person, she instantly warmed to Baxter and he to her, having never met each other, and now he sat half on her lap and half on the sofa, tongue lolling dangerously close to her fresh tea.

'Baxter!' I cautioned him, 'Careful with the house-guests!'

Simone smiled, muttered that he's no trouble, and petted him gently on the head. I hadn't seen Simone in so long. She looked well, much younger than her actual age. Having lost her own mother around five years ago, I'd expected her to look drawn and haggard, but she looked fine. I suppose five years is long enough to grieve the loss of someone, but it hadn't always been for me. I guess because the people I'd lost seemed to be taken too soon, gone in their prime.

She'd travelled light, and half her clothes seemed to be on her, despite the warm weather. As always, Simone had thrown together a strange concoction of clothes to form some kind of garish, almost nouveau-riche look, which to an innocent bystander would probably seem worthy of being punishable by law. She'd given me a big, warm hug in my doorway, motioned how nice it was to see me.

'How have you been?' she smiled up at me, Baxter now fully resting his head on her lap. Despite my upping the amount of dog biscuits he was having daily and even switching to a better, well-known brand, he seemed to be getting more lethargic rather than less. Simone would later tell me, when I asked her about this, that it was just the warmer weather causing Baxter to become sleepier, and not to worry, as her cats were much the same in summertime.

'Yes, good,' I replied, sipping from my own tea, 'You?'

Thankfully, she was no longer asking me if I wanted to join a local church. I think she had gotten the message when I had completely ignored that aspect of her own letters when writing my replies to her. Church remained a large part of her own life, though, and Greg's, as she exampled when she filled me on her own life now: 'Greg and I have been helping out at church,' she said solemnly. 'Distributing meal packages to the local community has been really important during the pandemic, and both of us have had the time to help out. Greg's been working from home since the lockdown started in March, and I've only been working three days a week myself. Still cleaning.'

Tactfully, Simone left the God/church chat there, and quickly moved on. It was very noble of her and Greg to help out in Brixton like that, and very much a Simone thing to do, but it wasn't really my bag. Simone knew that and didn't push any of it any further. We exchanged a few more niceties as I sat down next to her and Baxter on the sofa. We weren't yet completely at ease in each other's presence, so I perched on the sofa rather than fully relaxing into it. It had been so long since we had last seen each other. Still, as Lara had suggested it, this must be a good idea.

There was a brief silence, as Simone glanced around my living room, noticing the large bay window — 'lovely', she commented (Simone always liked traditional features and architecture) — the tasteful decor, the large array of newspapers (I read a lot of news, albeit not much in the way of books), the old-fashioned TV.

'Nice place you have here,' she said, followed by a smile and another, short silence. 'I'm sorry if...' she began. I tensed. She noticed my tension, and quickly added, 'I'm sorry if I wasn't the most understanding when you—'

She struggled for the words. I tried to read her face. We had never been overly close growing up, so it was hard sometimes to gauge precisely where she was going with things.

'When you... Y'know—' Her face strained to say the words, her eyeballs expanding with intimation. We were looking straight into each other's eyes for the longest period we had since she'd arrived. I didn't feel there was anything Simone had done overly wrong to me, so I genuinely, in that precise moment, didn't know what she was trying to apologise for.

'Came out!' She released those words all at once, in a flurry, then exhaled with relief. She looked quite funny, in her tasteless clothes and sipping carefully at her herbal tea. She took several sips now to avoid speaking again too soon, patted the dog a little to get him on side.

After a moment I laughed, a real belly laugh. Simone darted a look at me, mildly offended. I let her simmer for a moment then said: 'No trouble,' and I meant it, 'There's been enough pain since then to last us both a lifetime. Please, don't think about it any longer. No harm done.'

She paused, then little droplets of tears filled in her big, hazel eyes. She touched the skin of my left forearm lightly, next to one of my Sailor Jerry tattoos, brushed her hand away.

'Thank you,' she whispered, looking deep into my eyes, 'Thank you so much.'

* * *

We agreed Simone would stay for two weeks. It wasn't too long, and it wasn't too short. We had lots to catch up on, lots of old wounds to heal. Darone was currently staying at theirs, and

Simone thought the time would also give them both time to bond with each other, as well as us bonding together, too.

'Boy's time and girl's time,' she'd enthused, raising her hands in the air in excitement, her face a picture of forced pleasure.

'Don't push it,' I'd cautioned back, smiling.

Brixton

August 2002

I lit a spliff as Janine razed most of my hair away and T. Rex played in the background. Janine loved T. Rex. I was sick of T. Rex, but Janine was cool and currently transforming my look, so T. Rex it was. As her arms orbited my cranium in slow but definite circles, I caught glimpses of her inner forearms, the bruises left from a clenched, restraining hand. Adam had started knocking her about recently as their arguments intensified. I said nothing.

I hadn't heard a great deal from Kyle or Simone for a little while. Kyle and I had been back on speaking terms for the last few months (after he'd cold-shouldered me for leaving Simone's), however at this point in time there wasn't much to tell each other or talk about. He continued to not get on very well with Greg, but as far as I knew it wasn't anything major. He was itching to buy a moped, which he would be able to do soon enough, funds permitting. Elsa and Darone were still around, but I heard very little from them or what they were up to. Simone and I occasionally texted each other, but it was mostly just niceties and not a lot of in-depth discussion. It seemed as though everything was fine at her place.

My finished look was exactly what I'd been hoping for, and

I couldn't thank Janine enough. Her soft blue eyes admired her work in the mirror, her dimpled complexion giving way to a broad, natural smile. She touched the remnants of my hair, stroked it deeply and slightly scratched my scalp. It felt incredible. She paused, hand still on my head.

'I-er,' I started.

'Yes,' she finished, and we moved swiftly away from the mirror. Her living room was sizeable, but the floor was awash with clothes and rubbish, and it was sometimes problematic to find things amongst the clutter. We each managed to retrieve the things we had been looking for and finished our 'getting ready' routine. I caught a glimpse of myself in the hallway mirror as we were leaving. I didn't study myself often and didn't have time to now, but it felt like a moment to pause and to absorb myself. My tired eyes, even at sixteen, laid bare my struggles: struggles I would probably carry for most of my life. I was handsome — like Kyle, like Mum — with a softer face than I wanted, and deep, black eyes. Kyle and I both had chestnut brown hair, and where Kyle's was curly like Mum's, mine was straight as a dime. I touched my hair, my face, the smoothness of my jaw, and I contemplated a lot of things in that moment: things that had passed, things that were yet to pass.

'C'mon, darling,' Janine pressed, 'You got girls can look at you like that now.'

I smiled appreciatively and we left. The night itself was mildly triggering: they played a lot of '90s disco which put me in mind of times gone by. Mum loved '90s disco. The Spice Girls, Kylie, Madonna, Haddaway, Snap…! It all blared out of the giant speakers. I tried to shut the memories out and enjoy the experience. I got horrendously drunk the first time. The floor was sticky and the bar offered 'blow jobs' among other delightfully-named treats. 'Blow jobs' were thankfully just a drink. The atmosphere was electric and the air thick with anticipation. The bar itself smelt like poppers, which I guess would be no surprise. Drag queens swanned through from time-to-time, camp men in neon clothing hot on their trail. There weren't many lesbians, but enough women to make it worth my while to go. We got in because Janine knew one of the bouncers; everyone knew I was underage. It was a good night, the first of many at Cardinals. In my black t-shirt and ripped jeans, with my new short hairdo, I looked like any one of the small number of boyish lesbians in there. There were a handful of femmes to catch my eye, though not many. The club itself was in a really grotty part of Vauxhall: kebab shops, bookies, prostitutes, dim street-lighting; it all cosied up to me and my first experience of gay nightlife.

The second time we went I was shocked to bump into an old friend in the toilet. Laura. Laura from my Year 9 schooldays. She was fairly drunk and had eyeliner stains running down her cheeks. It didn't look like she had been crying — more that she was having a good time and as a result of that good time she had messed her make-up a bit. Her cheerful eyes suggested the same. I was surprised to see her; I didn't think she was gay, and I thought she'd want to avoid a place like this. She seemed so vanilla at school. She recognised me instantly and reached to touch my hair, pulling me closer to her.

'Chris!' she exclaimed, delighted to see me, 'You look amazing!'

She dug her fingernails into the back of my head, pulled my body right into hers, and went to whisper in my ear.

'You know I always liked you at school. You know I fancied you so much.'

She seemed quite drunk, and I found her behaviour slightly

childlike (more the mannerisms and facial expressions she used rather than what she was saying explicitly), but when she moved her body into mine it felt good. I hadn't experienced a woman moving against me like this, ever. She tipped my head back and looked into my eyes, her blue eyes darting backwards and forwards into mine. I had never been attracted to Laura, but in that moment, I knew that if she tried something on then I'd probably accept, out of curiosity as much as anything else. We were blocking one of the three sinks in the sink unit, and I could hear other lesbians muttering impatiently behind us, but I didn't care. I wanted experience. The other lesbians would understand: they were desperate for it, too. They were just perpetually jealous, as lesbians so often are. Just leave the loos with dirty hands, goddammit, we've all done it.

'I want to—' Laura started, then stumbled into the nearest cubicle, dragging me along with her. It was cramped, dark green and smelt horrific, but I was a willing participant. Laura slammed the door shut behind her and leaned against it. She started lifting up her top, and pulled down her bra to expose her breasts.

'Laura,' I tried to caution her, but she pulled me towards her again. 'Shut up,' she said, kissing me. Her tongue pressed into my mouth, searched around zealously for mine, and I reciprocated. I pressed against her in the cubicle, as her hands felt the fullness of my hips and arms. She reached for my hand, tried to guide it inside of her underwear. Here I stopped: though I felt aroused, Laura was clearly quite drunk, and I wasn't interested enough in her specifically to do this. She moaned in disappointment, kissing my neck. It felt good.

'You want to go someplace, and we can—' she started, but then acknowledged the negation in my eyes. 'Okay,' she reasoned, disappointedly, 'I get it.'

She looked forlorn, amidst the alcohol breath and watery make-up, but not too dismayed. She looked pretty, here in this green cubicle, her wavy blonde hair framing her delicate face. She was pretty, I just wasn't personally attracted to her, for whatever reason. In this moment, I wished I could be.

I forced a smile, to console her mood, and she buoyed, like a bobbing sea beacon, lifting up like a dandelion head in spring. I was inwardly glad we hadn't gone any further, though diplomatically didn't disclose this relief to Laura personally, and wished her a good rest of the evening. Looking back, she could well have been crying before to cause those make-up stains on her face. It was hard to know for sure, and she'd seemed so elated to see me that I was sure she was okay. If I'd had my time again, perhaps I'd have asked a few more questions. Why are you here? Are you even gay? Are you gay like I am? How long have you known?

I didn't see Laura on the gay scene at all after that, but occasionally saw her shopping in town with her mum or a friend. She didn't acknowledge me at all when I saw her, seemed to actively look away from me. Perhaps she was embarrassed about what had happened between us?

The rows between Janine and Adam intensified after Janine and I started going to Cardinals. On the few occasions I was alone with Adam, for whatever reason, there was a definite tension: something hung in the air, and the power balance was off. He would look at me in a way that seemed to hide its own anger, and I trod on eggshells around him. He would do things out of spite: hide the remote control, eat my food from the fridge, make lots of noise banging about in the kitchen when my room was adjacent to the kitchen and I was catching up on sleep from a late shift the night before. He and Janine seemed to fuck louder, for longer, when I was clearly in earshot, and I'd have to busy myself with something, or else leave the flat to go to buy something I probably didn't need. And he would watch me sometimes, let his eyes bore into me, made sure I registered his disgust. Men would do this often in my life, or else impose themselves in my space so easily and so dominantly that I was forced to acknowledge their presence, forced to accept their physical superiority. It was hard to stomach — men behaving like that around me — but harder still to try to change. I was best just to try to ignore it when it happened, then as now.

I knew what was coming before Janine said it.

'I think, maybe,' she looked tired, bruised and worn down, 'I think maybe you should leave.' She paused, looked for the disappointment on my face that wasn't there, that already knew this was coming. 'Adam's been struggling with us being—' She searched for the right word, 'Close. I think he's still getting over some stuff from his own past. I think his mum left his dad for another woman and so he's always a bit scared that might happen to him.' Another pause, then, 'I'm sorry.'

I shrugged. I had known this was coming and wasn't surprised. I could have been a bit more genial to Janine by way of reply, however it felt like a betrayal, and I knew she was letting him batter her about, which I struggled to respect her for. In hindsight I would tell myself that many women go through similar things, and it can be extremely difficult to leave an abusive partner. In hindsight I would tell myself that Mum had probably gone through similar, that this isn't Janine's fault, that she's the victim here, not the perpetrator. But in that moment, all I could offer was a shrug.

I packed my bags and admitted defeat, headed back to the

place I didn't want to have to go to, to surrender to old surroundings and familiar uncomfortabilities.

Janine stopped me on the way out.

'I'll always be your friend,' she proffered, her hand reaching over to brush my right forearm. Adam was out, otherwise she wouldn't have offered her touch in this way. I winced at the touch, moved my arm away. Saying nothing in response, I closed the door behind me.

* * *

Having not heard much from Simone or Kyle in a while, I figured things at Simone's would be relatively peaceful. Moving back in wasn't my first choice, but it was necessary until I could save up the funds for my own place. I had my heart set on my own little flat and would achieve it in time. Simone wouldn't mind me putting in the hours at the soft drink factory, and I was helpful around the house when not at work; certainly more helpful than Kyle.

I hadn't anticipated what I'd arrived to, Kyle and Greg at loggerheads every day, Kyle still smoking pot on the regular and now somehow managing to do it under Simone's very own roof. Simone didn't think anyone could hear but I heard her admitting to Greg that she was a little afraid of Kyle, that one time he'd threatened her with a knife. I struggled to believe this but still, it put a lot of things into perspective. I wanted closeness to Kyle again, but he was living in his own little world, choosing to lock himself in his room for hours on end. I enjoyed pot, but Kyle took it to another level. For me it was occasional fun with friends, for Kyle it was permanent escape. In a rare moment of comical relief, Simone half-heartedly voiced her despair about what I'd done to my 'lovely hair'.

I still went to Cardinals on the sly, and Gekkos. I'd tell Simone a slightly different shift time to my actual, then sneak off to a gay bar after work. The bouncers knew me now, and didn't mind that I was underage, as I was no trouble, and I got on with everyone. I didn't see Janine for a while, then I'd see her again and she'd be happy, then she'd go MIA again for a while, then she'd come back again, and so it continued. Whenever she resurfaced there were faint honey-yellow bruises on her arm that only a discerning friend would notice. I paid no heed and told her it was good to see her again. Adam, she professed, she was still madly in love with. Adam, she professed, would see her right.

Hull

August 2020

One of the things I like most about Simone is that she stress-smokes. Greg isn't supposed to know. She stress-smokes very occasionally and she also smokes sometimes when in the company of other smokers. It's so rare for her that she really doesn't need to feel that bad about it. She used to smoke more when she was a lot younger, she tells me, but managed to (mostly) quit.

'Don't tell Greg,' she always says, and said it now, as we sat together on two plastic garden chairs, 'Don't tell Greg what I'm up to.' As if she did it often. As if it was anything to feel overly bad about. That was Simone, all right: constantly feeling guilty about something.

It was still August 2020, and Simone had been with me for a week. We'd been having a jolly ol' time together, reminiscing the happy times of my childhood and teenage years, and cooking tasty food together. Cafés and restaurants had reopened since July, so we'd been able to enjoy some time out and to eat out together. It had all been very pleasant and cordial. I'd even told her about Siobhan, and that things had been going reasonably well between us. But it was getting to crunch time: at some point we'd have to talk more about the nitty-gritty things that had happened between us. Simone could sense this coming: perhaps that explained her furious puffing away on a Marlboro Red like the thing was gonna disappear if she didn't suck it hard enough. We were sitting outside one of my favourite cafés on Beverley Road. It had been a particularly warm summer and we had been blessed with some lovely weather over the last week. Today was no different, and a light, cool, August breeze whipped around our faces as we ate. Simone had a ham and cheese panini and a breakfast tea; me, a southern-fried chicken wrap and a white coffee.

'You know, Greg's always been really good to me.' As she said it, she looked up from her panini, searching for the disagreement in my expression. Simone was convinced that I hated Greg, I'm sure, but I really didn't. 'He's always cared about you and Elsa and Darone, and he cared about Kyle, too.'

I stopped eating, discomfort and annoyance flashing across my face. It wasn't that Simone had said anything wrong, or even that I didn't agree with her words, just that it was hitting a bit close to home. I didn't talk about Kyle much. I barely spoke to my therapist about him. It was all so, so repressed, buried deep down inside. It was something I could only talk about when very drunk, or never at all. And since I didn't drink very often anymore — and when I did, I tried not to drink too much — you would be wise to guess that I didn't talk about it often. Now Simone was bringing it all up, unprompted, unannounced. I knew this would happen, I knew we would need to go there. But right now? Couldn't we do this later?

'We really loved your brother,' Simone added, carefully. It was telling that she said 'we'. Her and Greg, Greg and her. They were a team. Though, I guess they always had been, since he'd come onto the scene. 'We tried so many things.'

Gone were the days when I would have retorted, 'well you should've tried a few more.' I wasn't angry anymore. I was mostly just numb. Numb and sad and at risk of wanting to get blind drunk if we ventured down this path too much further. I just gave a half-smile by way of reply. Simone nervously picked at her panini, unsure what to do or say next. I waited a few moments before breaking the silence myself.

'I know Greg isn't a bad person,' I reassured her, tentatively, 'I've never really thought that, not really. I just find it hard to talk about this.'

'Still?' Simone couldn't mask her surprise, though diplomatically recovered herself. 'I mean, yes of course. He was your brother. I'm sorry. Of course. This will always be a lot for you to talk about. Is there anything about it that you can talk about?'

I took a small, gentle bite from my wrap. I'd lost my appetite.

'Having lost both Kyle and Mum, I—' I stumbled for the words, then found them, eventually. 'I miss them both. They were both part of me but also part of a different life. It's all a lot to handle. I just wish I could erase all of the memories of it. I still have such vivid dreams.'

I had never really opened up to Simone properly, but perhaps this was the right time.

'I've been put on anti-anxiety medication, and I'm back with a therapist. There's so much to unpack.'

Simone's face grew lighter, as though a shadow had been lifted. There were no shadows, it was clear as day, but somehow, she looked lighter, brighter.

'I'm so pleased for you,' she offered, smiling. 'I'm so

pleased you are taking all of the right steps. Please know that for me, regards Kyle, there's a lot of guilt and pain there. I wish I could have done more. I wish Greg and I together could have done more. I couldn't face you that day you came round to talk to Greg. I was too eaten up by it all, the pain and the grief and the guilt. I still am sometimes. It was an awful time.'

I nodded understandingly, brushing away small tears from my eyes. Simone did the same. We ate the rest of our lunch in silence, though it wasn't an uncomfortable one. It was just nice to be, and to sit, together. In some ways it felt like a huge weight had been lifted, like Simone and I had pushed a huge boulder out of the way, and we could now be more of our true self with each other. We did a lot of people-watching and pet-watching (there were a fair few dog-walkers about).

Towards the end of our lunch, Simone took a few pensive sips of her tea, suddenly thoughtful again, suddenly wistful. I panicked inwardly, concerned that she might pounce on me with another deep subject matter. She snapped out of it somehow, and rallied, before asking: 'When are you next going to see your lady friend?' She searched for the right name. 'Siobhan, isn't it?'

'Yes,' I smiled naturally at the question, invigorated by the mere mention of the girl I like. 'Soon, I hope. We see each other every weekend, sometimes more frequently.' I wondered how much I could tell Simone of my fears, my hesitations. I'd never really opened up to her about my pain when Steph and I broke up, but now we'd just had a serious heart-to-heart with each other, and I was feeling inclined to be open with her. I didn't want to talk about Steph and bring up all of that baggage, but I did want to talk a bit more about my current amore.

'We haven't been intimate much yet,' I explained, testing the waters slightly with the more respectful option of 'intimate' rather than cruder language. 'I'm carrying so much around emotionally that I'm struggling to convert my feelings into action. I'm struggling to show her physically how much I like her.'

Simone paused, then nodded a few times understandingly. She didn't look like she was going to offer much advice — perhaps 'gay talk' was still a bit much for her. Finally, she proposed some advice:

'Just talk to her about what's going on with you emotionally. Tell her about your thoughts and your headspace,' Simone offered sagely, 'Once you feel truly connected to each other, the intimacy will come naturally.'

'Truly connected to each other.' It put me in mind of Simone's days of old, when she used to sing on the back steps, chucking vast waterfalls of chemicals on them while wearing hideous, tye-dye clothing. She'd looked like a pagan wicker woman at the time. Blow them all if she wasn't a die-hard Christian soul underneath all that awful clothing! At least she'd had a very tuneful and melodic voice.

'Thanks,' I replied. 'That's good advice.'

'Does she like your tattoos?' Simone asked, lightening the mood, 'And Baxter?'

'Yes,' I responded, heartily. Siobhan did like my tattoos very much, and Baxter. Simone however wasn't so big on tattoos. 'I guess you only like one of those items,' I teased.

Simone mock-grimaced slightly, chuckling, 'Whatever makes you happy!'

I wanted to ask her about the man in Norway: what had happened there? How come she stopped mentioning him when we got older? How come she only ever really mentioned him once to us? Did they ever get fully divorced? I decided that I'd opened up to Simone, so the least she could do was to offer a bit of the same back. I went for it.

'Simone?' I prompted, waiting for her acknowledgment.

'Yes?' She continued to look ahead at a nicely dressed woman daintily picking up her dog's poo from the pavement on the other side of the road.

'Whatever happened to that man in Norway?'

It was out there, faster than a bullet. It cracked the air and held Simone's attention, though she wouldn't admit it. This could be her undoing. If she was still married, wasn't Simone living in sin? Why wouldn't she marry Greg? Wouldn't her church feel that Greg and Simone should get married?

Simone sighed slightly, still watching the woman, who was moving towards a nearby bin, clutching the shit. I wondered if Simone secretly wanted to trade places and to clutch shit rather than answer my horrific question.

'We officially divorced a few years ago,' she stated coolly, as though it were not a big issue, 'But we were separated years before that. Greg and I just don't want to get married. Marriage can be such a horrible, restrictive thing. I had such a bad time with my first marriage that I just don't want to go through it again. The church we're with understand.'

It was as though she had read my mind, answering with such specificity. I nodded slowly, taking it all in. In fairness, Greg and Simone's church did seem like very nice people. They didn't seem as judgmental as Simone's first church, back in the day. It didn't make me want to go to church anytime soon, but perhaps it went some way to explain why Simone wasn't too arsed anymore about my being gay. Perhaps she was just in a better, more tolerant headspace. And after all, there was affair-gate, which meant Simone was hardly whiter-than-white herself in terms of her own history.

Remember? Affair-gate? Simone shagging that married man?

None of this was, of course, relevant now, and as I looked over at Simone, all I felt was love, as her strawberry blonde hair whipped around her face in the summer breeze. I thought of all the pain Kyle and I had caused her over the years, and how readily she was always able to offer forgiveness for those things. I vowed to offer her the same.

'Come on,' I said, tapping the outdoor table gently twice, 'Drink up, let's go. This café will start to think we want to live here.'

Brixton

November 2003

It was November 2003, and I was turning eighteen. Already I had a bit of a reputation on the Vauxhall gay scene. I would meet a pretty girl, finger her stupid in the toilets, then pie her off the next day. It wasn't right, but in many ways, it was keeping me sane. So, by my eighteenth birthday, in the prime of my youth and glory days, I was already a substantial force to be reckoned with: the crème de la crème of baby butch.

Only a few months prior, an older friend of Elsa's had been in Cardinals the same night as me and had caught wind of my antics, then told Elsa — who amazingly, in the right circumstances (read: gossip), could find a voice — and Elsa subsequently told Simone. Simone wasn't best pleased, but considering I was likely her favourite of the motley gang of castaways under her roof (bar Greg), chose to let it go. From what I gather Greg even found my escapades somewhat amusing, which was quite insulting. I would (hopefully) be fingering women for the rest of my life — that was the aim. Why is that funny if it's my life?

I had saved up enough for my own place and started looking around. The aim was to put down a deposit somewhere small. Around December 2003, though, I started to wonder if I wanted to stay in Brixton after all? I didn't have a girlfriend yet, and wasn't likely to anytime soon with the reputation I was accumulating. Maybe it would be better to travel for a bit, gain some life skills, or else just see where my nose led me, rather than fixing myself to one set place? Where would be the benefit in that? If I bought my own place I was tied to Brixton, at least for a little while, and I started to realise that right now might not be the best time to settle down. So, I bided my time, and decided to rent a flat instead.

It was a cute little joint: not far from Simone's and with a touch of grass out front. Kyle had a moped now and would race it around the local streets; sometimes I looked out my front window to see my own brother tearing past, not a care in the world. I told him to drop in sometimes, say hello. Did he bother? I had a ground-floor flat, which they say women shouldn't have, but I didn't always see myself the way others did. Probably there were times in my life where being aware of my own femaleness wouldn't have been a bad thing, but in terms of living arrangements I just wanted to get by and feel comfortable in the home I lived in.

Upstairs was a middle-aged man with a bunch of tattoos and a Norton. His Norton sometimes woke me up in the mornings, but I never complained. He was a bit scary looking.

Seeing his host of tattoos made me want to get my own and I started to frequent the local parlour, which conveniently was just round the corner from my flat. I liked those Sailor Jerry-style pirate tattoos, so got a bunch of them, one or two of a naked or semi-naked lady. It was a complete waste of money, but I was young and reckless, with plenty of bare skin to add colour and life to. I messed with my hair, too, all different colours. Got myself a cheap Ford saloon car — 1998 model — only went up to sixty on the A-roads but I was happy enough. Increased my hours at the soft drink factory. Smoked twenty a day but cut out the pot and pills. It was a life, and it was mine. Sometimes Janine came over and we just hung out. She told me Adam was treating her better now, but I'd heard that one before. I just drank and listened. My living room was cosy and a good room to entertain a friend in. Meanwhile, Kyle wasn't up to much. Kyle wasn't even working, though I didn't talk to him often.

I got my first girlfriend in late January 2004. She was called Steph and she was a couple of years older than me, non-smoker, bit of a gym bunny. Beautiful figure. Kyle came round to mine two months into my relationship with Steph, wanted to have a catch-up. It was March 2004. I was more than willing, having made several attempts in recent months to initiate the same but hearing little back from him.

He cut through the niceties and told me he wasn't doing well. Wasn't inclined to take care of himself or bother getting a job. Was rowing lots with Simone and Greg. Wanted to know if he could kip on my sofa for a while. Oh and—

'Why did you never tell me you were gay?'

It came out of nowhere: we'd only had a couple of lagers and hadn't really been sat down for long when he hit me with this curveball. Steph was out but had moved in with me pretty quickly; we had decided that we'd try to make a real go of things. Lesbians do that, don't they? Move in together quickly.

'I thought we were close. Why didn't you ever tell me you were gay?'

I sipped my lager. I needed a moment to think through my answer. I looked out my dirty, shabby net curtains to Kyle's navy moped on the drive. He'd chugged up to my flat on it, parked on the scant grass outside and left it on its metal stand. The bike was scratched heavily and looked past its best. I wondered how he afforded it with no job or income of note, but decided not to ask about that right now.

'Even fucking Elsa knew before I did.'

He actually used a racial slur to describe Elsa — something he did readily when wishing to reference Elsa or Darone — but I chose to ignore the slur on this occasion. Sometimes I upbraided him: this was not the time.

I told him he'd been going through it a lot the last few years, that I hadn't wanted to overload him, and my being gay might be a difficult pill for him to swallow. He didn't understand this hypothesis, and I didn't feel up to clarifying. Kyle offered me a fag, but I told him I was cutting back because Steph wanted me to. He grimaced and muttered, 'Under the thumb.' I chose to ignore him.

'Haven't you got a bird at the moment?' I asked. Kyle always had someone on the go.

No, he replied, not at the moment. Not for a while. That wasn't like Kyle.

'Look, you can kip here a bit, but not all the time. Steph won't like it.'

In fact, from what I'd told her of him, Steph didn't like Kyle at all. Thought he was a waste-of-space layabout. She didn't use these exact words to me, but I could tell she was thinking it, and sometimes, so was I. We both hurt from losing Mum, but Kyle and I handled things very differently.

Over the next few months, things were strained in my flat. Steph would come home from her hellish call centre job and want to chill out on the sofa, just with me, to find Kyle still there. It didn't make for a happy situation. I tried to play peacemaker, but it did no good. Steph bit her tongue every time, out of respect for me, and I didn't want her to have to feel like that anymore. Plus, we were thinking of moving somewhere else. Steph didn't think much of my neighbour (the tattooed chap upstairs), and I hadn't really studied the flat in as much detail as I thought I had. Steph, who was from a nice part of North London near Camden Town (not originally, but certainly in recent years), knew how to spot a turd better than I did, and could see the patches of damp in the corners of the living room, the mould stains on the back porch, the bad plumbing job in our compact kitchen, the wear-and-tear of the place, the gaps and the faults. It was a 1960s build which had already started to fall into disrepair and, where I had loved just having my own place, Steph was more discerning and was able to see the bad bits. Plus, the landlord wouldn't let us decorate, so we were stuck with white walls and royal blue carpets throughout the entire apartment. We did at least have new white goods and most of the appliances in the kitchen were relatively recent, but Steph thought it best we find someplace new.

At dinner one night in early summer 2004, as we sat on the sofa together, the day's burning, orange sun setting over the bins and grey, terraced houses outside, Steph pushed her glasses further up her button nose: the cute thing she always did when she had a difficult topic to broach. Kyle wasn't around on this occasion and Steph had made us a lovely leek and bacon risotto; she was an excellent cook. We had a side-lamp on and the telly on low: *Hollyoaks*. We both loved *Hollyoaks* and I'd watched it since it first aired in late 1995. I knew all of the plotlines, all of the sub-plotlines, all of the juicy details. Trashy TV was an integral part of the earliest years of my life — that and *Golden Girls* — and I wasn't about to abandon my love for utter trash now.

'Nothing against Kyle,' she started, as she always did in our conversations these days, 'But more against this place.' She looked around the dusty living room plaintively, before continuing, 'Perhaps we could move elsewhere? There are some great places in Clapham. We could afford it on our joint pay, and maybe even get a little cat, and maybe, maybe we could make it just us?'

It pained me to hear Steph say this, but it pained me even more to know that she wasn't very happy with Kyle around. I loved Steph and I wanted her to be happy. I didn't take long to think about my answer. Clapham was closer to both of our workplaces, and a nicer area than where we were now. I was paying very little in rent in my Brixton flat and could probably have afforded to pay a bit more for somewhere nicer. I was just trying to be careful with my money, but I could afford to increase my budget on accommodation, for sure, especially if we were both pitching in. Steph's job was salaried compared to my hourly wage, and we could easily afford a place of a similar size in Clapham.

'Yeh of course babe,' I told her, with little hesitation, 'You got it.'

I broke the news to Kyle, who didn't take it well, but who had by this point started up with a new girlfriend, who he was seeing a lot of. Things remained at boiling point between him and Greg, but he could stay at Emily's sometimes (his girlfriend's name), to take the heat off things. Provided he and her didn't break up, I figured he would probably be okay.

It was amazing to get my first place with Steph. We got the keys in August 2004. It was a first floor flat in a small, red bricked building on the corner of busy Clapham High Street, overlooking the shops and lazy shoppers walking idly by in the summer sun, their cigarette fumes wafting up to us. It was cosy and we could play around a bit with the decor as Steph had asked this to be included in our contract. She started painting the walls all sorts of nonsensical colours, and, despite violet being her alleged favourite colour, displayed a propensity towards lime green. We painted together and she messed my overalls with paint before we collapsed on the floor together and got frisky. She bought a painting of a white deer which I hung in our bedroom and stared at sometimes. The deer looked so proud but also kind of sad, with a strong, able physique but tired, wary eyes of black. Its backdrop was a litter of trees, a throng of bushes, a pillow of grass, but it stood alone. Strong and alone. Tired and alone.

I decided against getting a cat too soon, as we were still only renting rather than buying a place, and we'd still only been together a matter of months. Steph was more comfortable in her skin without Kyle around, and we found more opportunities to be intimate together. I had cut down on the number of cigarettes I was smoking, and even started going to the gym a bit, though I didn't go with Steph, as I've always seen exercise as a bit of a solo activity. In the evenings we would relax and unwind. It was the closest to heaven I'd been in a long while and I've truly never been closer since.

Hull

September 2020

It was sad to say goodbye to Simone, but I felt we'd bonded and finally healed over old wounds. On her way out, Simone suggested I move back to Brixton, said there were so many people there who still loved me and missed me. I thought of seeing all the old faces again, Janine, other old friends, Steph and whichever boring, middle-class man she'd married. I thought better of it.

'I'm okay,' I said, gratefully adding, 'but thanks for the suggestion. Baxter prefers it here. We've a home here now.'

'I see that,' she'd replied, looking wistfully around the parts of my home she could see from my front door, 'Well you're always welcome.'

I thanked and hugged her, wishing her safe travels, and we said goodbye. Simone had wanted to hug for a long time, but I had never been comfortable with overly long hugs.

Before she'd left, I'd assured Simone that I'd talk to Lara about all of the unfinished feeling I was holding inside regards Kyle, and I made true on that promise. I scheduled to speak to Lara ahead of our usual time, still over Zoom for now, and made a mental list of all the things I wanted to go over with her.

A few days later, in September 2020, Lara and I sat down

together to chat over video. She popped up on Zoom, her pale-yellow living room wall nicely silhouetting her slim frame. I knew it was her living room; her tabby cat sometimes slept discreetly on the sofa behind her, and a potted plant was ever-present on the soft, oak coffee table. It looked like a nice home. I didn't know a lot about Lara's life, but I knew that she lived in Brough. Her cat looked old and slept a lot. The whole time we had been having our therapy sessions over Zoom rather than in-person, I hadn't seen her cat stir once. What kind of life must that be, to sleep all day? Perhaps, of course, the cats themselves enjoy it.

'Hey!' Lara chirped breezily, coffee placed in front of her on a coaster, 'You wanted to talk ahead of time?'

'Yes please,' I said, answering the inevitable. I mean, we were already here over Zoom, having arranged an emergency session. It was pretty clear that I was in need of some urgent-ish therapy.

'When you're ready,' she encouraged calmly, sipping gently from her coffee as I found the words.

I told her about losing Kyle, about how it had happened. How even a motorbike passing by reminds me of him. How I should've been there for him more. How he never reached out in his darkest moments. How I felt guilty for that. I told her about losing Mum, about how certain music or specific songs from the '90s reminded me of her. That 1984 Tina Turner song. How I wasn't sure I would get over either of them. How I would still have vivid dreams about them both, even while on medication. I recalled specific memories of each of them: I remembered talking late into the night at Simone's with Kyle. Just chatting, chatting, chatting. Pranking Mrs Crabby. The man who came into my room once and, though he didn't touch me as Mum had warned him away from me, had left me feeling shaken and disturbed. How all of these feelings and memories were clogging me up and making me struggle to connect with Siobhan. How it had been good to see Simone, but something was still missing. How a part of me was wondering if I should move back to Brixton after all, considering I didn't have a mortgage or any major ties here. How a huge part of me still missed Steph, even after all these years. How I wish I'd told Kyle sooner that I was a lesbian, how I should have given him more of me. Should've protected him and offered him more to cling to, instead of leaving him out to dry.

'Wow,' Lara replied, after a short while, 'There's a lot to unpack there. Thank you for sharing with me. A good portion of these things will take you years to work through. But let's do what we can today to begin your healing process.'

I smiled sadly. She put her coffee down and stared at an indistinct point past her laptop, somewhere in the distance.

'Sometimes as well,' I started, Lara immediately looking back through the screen at me, 'Sometimes I worry I might go the same way as them,' I said. 'Just to be near them again. Sometimes I think I might be tempted to join them.'

Lara looked alert now, ears cocked like a cat's would if hearing a scurrying noise while out hunting. Not sure if her own cat ever knew anything of that, 'hunting'.

'Are you experiencing suicidal thoughts at all?'

Oh no, here we go. The dreaded questions. The psychiatrist's chair. Soon she would call the emergency services, have me dragged away in a straitjacket. I knew I wasn't likely to go the same way that Kyle and Mum had as I was more of an 'earth' soul; even in desperate, unbearable times, a part of me was resolute, heavy, weighted, anchored. Kyle and Mum lacked these traits. They were air-bound, ethereal souls. Never quite here, never fully present. Aware of other and constantly striving to reach it.

'No, no,' I pressed, almost pleadingly, 'I just mean that I feel lonely. I wonder where they are now, and what it must be like to be with them. And besides—' I paused, searching for the right words. 'It's not like I know where Mum actually went.'

This was a weightier sentence that I had intended it to be. Literally and metaphorically and personally and emotionally: for all of the above, I had no idea where Mum had gone.

I told Lara about the time I found Mum alone in bed, blood on the sheets, empty bottles and cocaine stalking her around the mattress.

'That's a lot of trauma there,' Lara consoled. 'You have done amazingly well to cope with so much of this basically entirely on your own.'

She smiled at me sympathetically through our virtual conversation. She paused for a bit, then said, 'You should talk to Siobhan about all of this.'

I nodded. Lara was probably right.

'Siobhan needs to know these things if you are getting serious with each other, which, considering we are still in a partial lockdown and possibly heading for a second major one, I seriously hope you are. I don't want to lecture you when you are already feeling a bit distressed, but people really aren't meant to see much of each other at the moment unless they are exclusively in a bubble with that person. I recommended you see Simone because I do feel that was vital to your emotional health at the time. I still feel that way and think it did you a serious amount of good. But this being said, we really can't treat meeting up with people as casual yet. You and Siobhan need to decide soon whether you are all in or all out. And I suggest you ask her soon. Perhaps ask her before you tell her about all of your pain. You don't want to tell her all of your past experiences then ask her if she still wants to stick around. If you do it that way round, and she rejects you, I'm worried your pain levels will grow to be exponentially higher.'

Lara looked deeply concerned when saying all of this. It felt good to know that she was 'on my side' in some way. You can never really know how your therapist feels about you, but I think Lara liked me. Certainly, I hoped that she liked me.

'See her sooner rather than later,' Lara finished.

I knew she was right. I talked to her a little more about mundane things, about work and other things, before Lara brought the conversation back to the main focus of the emergency consultation.

'You know, family events and the sort of trauma you have been through may never fully heal,' she counselled. 'You will always feel a degree of pain. It's learning how to cope with that pain and how to learn to channel it appropriately and in the least painful way possible, rather than having the pain channel you. You need to be the master. You're in charge, always. Now tell your head that.'

Lara made me tell my own head that I was in charge, three times. I wasn't really into performative tasks like that, so it was a little uncomfortable for me, but I obliged nonetheless.

'And ask your GP if you need to be on anything like antidepressants,' she advised, 'I'm not a doctor so I can't diagnose you, but it's possible that the anti-anxiety meds for your dreams aren't enough. You should ask your doctor about depression, too. See if that's not something you might have, and whether you need to take anything for it.'

Simone had been on antidepressants for years, and I knew other people who had taken them and never been able to stop taking them. I didn't want a life addicted to paroxetine.

'Maybe,' I replied, shrugging, 'I know a lot of people take those and never come off them.'

'Fine,' she reasoned, exhaling slightly, 'But at least talk to your doctor about how to manage your depression outside of therapy.'

I agreed to do this. Lara asked after a few other things in my life, such as Baxter and Darone. Baxter was a dog, and he was fine. Darone was a troubled young man and possibly less fine. We spoke sometimes but not very often. He was still finding his feet. I was still finding mine.

She asked how my time with Simone had gone, and was pleased to hear it had gone smoothly and had been constructive and healing to both of us.

'She's family,' Lara added knowingly, 'She'll always be a support net for you should you need it. Remember that when things get dark.'

Wrapping up the session, I agreed to the steps Lara had put in place for me, an almost prerequisite for emergency therapy.

'You must always have a plan out,' Lara espoused the cat for once raising its head, for the first time ever during these Zoom sessions, as if in a display of solidarity and support towards its owner's values and beliefs. 'You're inside of a box right now, but those walls are largely self-imposed. You can push them away. Even in these crazy times, you can push them away. The sky's the limit, Chris.'

It was all very rousing, but seeds of doubt remained in me still. Above all, I would never understand what my relationship with Steph had been about, what it had meant to Steph and why I never got the answers I needed. Why she'd left me, what I'd done so wrong, why she chose a man instead. Intrinsically, and in-keeping with that natural sixth sense therapists have (a skill well-honed from years of psychology study, I'm sure. Despite her youngish age, Lara had most psychology credentials going), Lara added, while looking at me intensely,

'Some things we will never have the answers to. Never, ever. Even if we could ask those persons ourselves, we might never get the answers we need. They might not give an honest reply, or else they may give us an answer we can't make head nor tail of. We just have to move on. Grieve, take time to grieve, then move on. We are our own limitations, and we are our own successes. We must fight for ourselves, for our futures. You, Chris, must fight for you. The others, I'm afraid, are gone. Your future is not gone and only you have the power to change it. Make it amazing, please. Make it incredible. Leave every other last damn thing behind.'

Clapham

August 2005

The summer we lost Kyle, August 2005, I'd been rowing lots with Steph. I'd started going back to the bars again, professing I missed my friends, and she grew agonisingly jealous. Truth was, we'd lost a bit of the spark between us, and I wanted to be around other women again. I wasn't going to cheat on Steph and I was still furiously attracted to her, but I was getting bored. Our relationship was getting stale. I was only nineteen, and I needed a bit more entertainment than I was getting. Even at twenty-one, Steph was ready to settle down. I'd thought I was, but time had proven otherwise. We were still amicable and romantic, and I still loved our life together on the whole, but something wasn't there. I was too young for this to be the start of the rest of my life. Deep down, Steph knew how I felt, even though I didn't tell her; even though I just drank down at Gekkos instead of pouring my heart out to her. Steph would buy sexy lingerie and I'd make love to her sometimes, though not as often as we used to. I had a piece of me missing. I had something left to do before I could accept this being the rest of my life, and I couldn't tell you what that 'something' was then, or now, but I knew it in my innermost being. I knew that Steph and that life wasn't my forever. I just knew it.

In the last few months, Kyle had really gone off the rails. Emily had broken up with him, and I heard from Simone that he'd threatened Greg with a knife. He'd upped his drug use, been arrested several times for cocaine possession. He'd been sleeping rough because Simone and Greg refused to let him indoors but similarly refused to call the police on him. The police found him in the grassland we used to go with Mum, the fields behind the disused industrial park outside of the city. He'd been missing for three days before he was found. Simone was distraught with worry, but even more distraught at the actuality of the situation. I'd never thought I'd lose him like this. He hadn't reached out to me once while sleeping rough. Why didn't he just call? Why didn't he let me take care of him?

I think he'd always found life not quite enough, had always wanted something more. Something in him had always yearned for a reality beyond that which was on offer to him. Life had tried to restrain him and couldn't.

I was overwhelmed with confusion and grief and spent hours and hours drinking in Gekkos. Even more hours than I was before. When I got home, Steph had a bunch of questions I couldn't answer. I slept on the sofa. Steph and I didn't have sex for weeks. It was the longest we went without intimacy. When I finally slept with her, I started crying halfway through, and she just held me in her arms for hours as the cool morning light drifted in through our bedroom window. There was a breakfast café only a few doors down and the smell of bacon rolls wafted into our home as I rested on Steph's breast and cried as she stroked my hair.

I had lots of questions for Simone and Greg, and they didn't always come out in the kindest way, but I needed answers. Why weren't they there for Kyle more? Why didn't they tell me what was going on?

One time, I went round to Simone's place to speak to them about everything that had happened. When I got there Greg made me a cup of tea and told me Simone wouldn't be joining us. Why, I demanded to know. Because she was too upset, Greg had replied. Because she was dealing with a lot of grief and guilt herself.

Greg told me that Kyle had been unbearable to both of them for many years, that they'd tried everything to help him. Kicking him out had been the absolute last resort. Simone had even tried to arrange new therapy for him, but none of it was enough. He was beyond help.

'No one is beyond help,' I countered, in an anguished cry, 'No one is beyond help from their family.'

Greg sighed a deep, troubled sigh. He explained that Kyle's violence had really climbed to new levels in recent months. That they'd tried everything. Finally, he let his hands go, fall to his sides, and slumped back in his chair. There was a long silence. I took in the room, and I took in Greg. He was a handsome man: tall, reasonably well-built without being podgy, with strong, defined features on his face. I could see what Simone saw in him. I looked around the home I'd known for so many years, photos of Kyle and I now replaced with photos of Simone and Greg. They'd even taken down the photos of Elsa and Darone, who were still under their roof. Perhaps they both just wanted peace, regretted Simone ever taking us on now that she had Greg to make her happy. Greg with the deep Scottish accent, deeper red hair, Christian faith and steady job. I buried the thought: none of it would make anything better, none of it would bring Kyle back.

I remained angry with Simone and Greg for a long time — out of denial as much as anything else — and was unable to help with funeral preparations. It hurt too much. Simone sorted everything, while I went home to Steph and cried for what felt like an eternity.

On the day of the funeral, Steph and I took ourselves with heavy hearts over to Simone's. Her street looked the same as ever, pristine and homely, with the same, self-sufficient neighbours trundling around merrily with their dogs. Simone's 1930s terraced, redbrick house looked clean and inviting behind the leafy, Brixton street. Outside the house, on the road itself, leaves danced in the wind, but no rubbish. Simone's dirty grey SUV had been replaced by Greg's smart, blue Vauxhall Astra, while behind his car sat a little yellow Mini car Simone had invested in.

Steph squeezed my hand tightly and kissed my head. I was a good three inches shorter than her so kissing me on the head was relatively easy for her. We looked to the pale green front door of Simone's house and she emerged, strawberry blonde hair flying in the wind, whipping around her face. Her hazel eyes caught mine across the street and she smiled a kind smile, offered a conciliatory wave. I lifted my hand in reciprocation. Several feet behind Simone, emerging after a short while, came her mother, who I'd met on several occasions, usually at Christmas. When Kyle, Elsa, Darone and I were much younger, and still only kids, Simone's mother had often joined us for the whole Christmas season. This was pre-Greg and pre-dramas-with-Greg.

Simone's mother — who we only really knew as just that, 'Simone's mother' — was someone I had always known as a stoic, silent lady. She was kind-hearted like Simone but spoke much less. Where Simone threw herself at things and at life, her mother watched from the sidelines and preferred a more reserved approach. We knew little of her, and little of her background. But she was there, drinking brandy with Simone, watching us, sitting playing awful family board games with us, in some of the most formative years of our lives. And now here, as we buried Kyle, her dignified, restrained manner was an appropriate and welcome addition among the mourners.

It was a small ceremony at Simone's church, and she opted for Kyle to be cremated. I had rightly been consulted on this beforehand and agreed on cremation. Greg delivered a small speech. For what it was worth, it was a lovely service. Small and discreet, but still meaningful. At the wake I spoke to a few members of Simone's church and entertained their small talk; Steph was better at this, and people warmed to her easily. A lady dressed in deep burgundy complimented Steph's jewellery. After enduring as much of the social niceties as could be deemed polite without so minimal as to be rude, Steph and I made our excuses and slipped out. Back at the flat I cried and cried until I thought I might have no tears left to give, as Steph cradled me in her slender arms.

Hull

September 2020

I turned up to Siobhan's house in my battered-up Ford Fiesta, a bouquet of sunburnt orange and yellow dahlias hidden on the backseat under my jacket. I was shaking with nerves, and feeling like I was on the cusp of something, like this was a pivotal, 'make-or-break' moment. It felt like the beginning of times, it felt like the end of times.

I honked my horn and sat, thinking. Things had been really crazy over the last few months. I'd started following more women's rights movements — not participating in them, per se, but 'keeping up' with their news — and things were looking very bleak. DV had been on the rise for some time, women were losing their jobs all over the country, women's incomes were suffering immensely up and down the nation. Lara always recommended I get involved in more groups to cure my loneliness, but I wasn't ready just yet to participate actively in anything political. I wasn't a bra-burner yet. But I was scared. Scared for myself, scared for the women in my life. I'd experienced prejudice, of course I had. I'm a visibly lesbian woman. Sometimes I think I've taken the hit in terms of healthcare, or treatment down the local shops, or when being served in the pub, or general day-to-day kindness, or that vague government-imposed rhetoric: 'opportunities'. Yeh, that's right. I think I've been shafted on 'opportunities'. I think people see a butch lesbian woman and they treat them like shit. I think that's happened to me. Now a pandemic is here to make things worse. To make both my present and my future worse. Because women in general have been hurt over the last few years, but women like me will be hurt even more because we don't fit the mould. Men hate women like me. Not all men, but a good portion of them. And do you know why? Because we don't entertain them, and we don't want to be with them sexually. And there you have it: the world in a nutshell. Men rule it. Women who are prepared to oblige those men come second and the rest of us? We're bloody screwed.

Siobhan emerged from her doorway as a vision in pink, beaming through the early-autumn air. She had a cardigan pulled tightly around her and the light breeze whipped her hair in front of her lovely eyes. Pulling her hair back, she scurried over to the car. I buried my worldly ponderings and produced the flowers, quick as a flash, as she opened the passenger door.

'Oh, how sweet,' she gushed, pulling herself into the car and reaching over to give me a peck on the cheek. 'They're just my colour.'

I flushed as pink as her dress with the kiss and she looked proudly on at her work. I started the engine and drove her to a secluded spot near the Humber Bridge. All the way she had the window down, the September winds rushing in to touch Siobhan as much as I wanted to. Again, she wore her make-up delicately and carefully. Again, she knew how to tempt without giving the game away.

Once stationary, romantically overlooking the River Humber from some nearby grassland, I moved to kiss her, but I mean really kiss her. I wanted to take her there and then, on the backseat. I was bursting with desire, and we hadn't seen each other for over a week. The country was looking like it might go into a full lockdown again, and I wanted to have her now. Now I was ready for sex, now I was ready for commitment. I was lonely and needy, and she looked incredible. If I hadn't needed her before like this, then I could only apologise; now I needed her. Please, Siobhan, please. Reciprocate. Give me what I need. I had thought lately of our first time: frantic, feverish, desperate, passionate, sexy. I had thought of removing her panties and tasting her. I had thought of how good she would taste, of how it would feel to then move inside her. I was overcome with emotion and desire. I prayed she would want this, too.

Mid-snog, Siobhan pushed away from me, and it took all of me to hold back. I was confused.

'Mmm?' I asked, not really wanting to hear the answer. 'Is something wrong?'

She sidled away from me slightly, so that she could compose herself. I'd smudged the light rouge of her lips, added more blush to her cheeks.

'You said a couple of months ago that you needed to work through some things,' Siobhan started, anxiously. I could tell she was being as measured as possible with her words. 'I want to know about those things if I'm to be your girlfriend. You haven't even—' She looked out the window, gave an exasperated shake of her head before turning back to me. 'You haven't even asked me to be your girlfriend. I don't know what any of this is. I haven't known for a while. I'm—' She hesitated, clearly wanting to soften the blow as much as possible, not hurt me. 'I'm back on dating apps.'

I sighed deeply, raised my hands to my head, and sat back in my chair. Clutching my head, I leant into the footwell and breathed deeply, in and out. This was a disaster. This was exactly what I did not want to happen.

'I've been talking to a couple of guys. I just want some kind of commitment. I feel ready for a relationship.'

It took a while for me to respond, to find the words for my disappointment. Why had she dressed up like this? Why did she look so beautiful if not to excite me? What was the point of this meeting? Why was she choosing to hurt me like this?

My eyes welled before I could stop them, and I turned my face to the glass. Siobhan had seen this before I could fully hide my pain. She moved closer to me, put a hand on my thigh.

'Hey,' she moved closer to me, whispering in my ear. 'Hey, sshh. I know, I know it hurts. I know you want me.'

She came closer still, let her breath dance on my left ear, so close that the heat was turning me on. I wanted her to surprise me, to lick my ear gently, to give me something of her that was wet. I was hurting but I was aroused. I was feeling so much raw energy and emotion all at once that I know that if she asked, I would fuck her there and then. I needed to release the tension inside of me. I needed to make love to her.

Siobhan continued to breathe into my ear, her breaths deepening and intensifying. She licked the top of my left earlobe and undid her seatbelt, climbing over the gearstick panel to sit on top of me, her face looking down on mine. We kissed passionately and she ran her hands through my short hair, intensifying my arousal. I reached to put my right hand up her dress, hoping to slip my finger inside of her, desire burning so hotly in my crotch that I longed for a penis I could love her with. I thought of her breasts, how much I wanted to see them and touch them and kiss them. She reached down again, to whisper in my ear.

'You want me?'

'Mmm,' I signalled, trailing off.

'Then you need to talk to me.'

Siobhan climbed off of me as quickly as she had gotten on; the air in which she had once occupied hung close and tight around me. I looked ahead into the distant grey of the Humber River and thought of darkness and the sudden loss of intimacy. Siobhan curled herself neatly into the passenger seat.

'You want me like I want you, but you won't talk to me.'

I was silent for a long while. I didn't feel frustration much anymore, after years of loss. I didn't really feel anything. I had hoped that physical intimacy with Siobhan would bring something back, but now she was denying me even that. I wasn't sure who was the victim here: her for my lack of openness, or me for the sex she had dangled in front of me and then taken away so sharply. I almost pitied myself, but I knew she was right. I'd have to be open with her sometime.

We sat in the late summer heat as I looked for the words. They weren't there.

'You know, I really think a lot of you,' I started, truthfully, 'I'm just not sure how ready I am to tell you everything.'

There was a wall there, inside of me, built up. Built up through years of hurt and denial, both self-imposed and externally so. There was a need to physically love Siobhan but not emotionally connect with her too much. I didn't want to show any weakness, wanted to be strong. Both Lara and Simone would have counselled me to tell Siobhan everything, all of the hurt and all of the loss, and indeed both of them had already counselled me with this advice, but for the life of me I couldn't find the words nor the heart to tell her it all. It wasn't there. My words weren't there.

I would have told her so much, but I just couldn't. I remember once telling Lara, not so long ago, that I wished that people would just open up to me, but when it came to the crunch, when it came to me opening up to someone else, to gain that intimacy, that trust, I just couldn't do it. What was wrong with me? Why couldn't I tell Siobhan about all of my past?

'Just take me home,' she said, sighing. I sighed too, my eyes still fixed on a part of the river where the riverbed could just be seen under gentle waves, the shallow bed home to a few lonely rocks. I longed to talk to her, felt compelled to talk to her so she could become my girlfriend, but the words weren't there. I was a coward, through and through.

'Shit Chris you're thirty-five and you can't find the words!' Her frustration built up and she kicked at the floor of my car. 'What was this even meant to be, you and I? Where was this even going?'

Tears started to well up in her own eyes now, mostly out of anger with herself, for holding out for me for this long.

'I've waited so long for you and for what? I'm not even your girlfriend yet. Take me home.'

Even as she spoke, I couldn't find the response she needed. I just hung my head and inwardly hoped for more time.

'Take me home.'

The time was up; I had to take her home. The drive back to Siobhan's place was long and quiet: I left the radio off. We had the windows down so that the September air could whip in and out and heal us where we couldn't heal ourselves. Each slight of breeze touched my head and my heart.

I pulled into Siobhan's driveway and she steeled herself

enough to look at me. When I didn't return the look, she muttered quietly but audibly enough for me to know she meant it: 'It's over.'

I let my heart tense and then drop; I didn't look at her. I counted the blades of grass in her garden as she removed herself from the car and away into the house. She left the bouquet on the seat. I drove home, sat on the road outside my house, and cried for almost an eternity, the once-beautiful dahlias seeming to wilt before my eyes.

Clapham

October 2006

The year following Kyle's death, I had terrible flashbacks and nightmares. I kept returning to the day we tried to search for Mum amongst the rubble: the day we knocked on the door of her old place, then I turned to Kyle, his eyes bulging with anticipation and desperation and hope, saliva building in his mouth, the thrill of cocaine already leaving traces on his muscle memory, saying, 'I'm coming for you. I'm coming to reel you into my claws. You will beg for me, you will beg for my sweet release. You will not survive this.' I'd wake up in hot sweats, pillows damp with sweat, Steph on the other side of the bed, struggling to sleep herself through my night-time anguish.

She'd struggle to drag me out of Gekkos, and when I wasn't in Gekkos, I was at work. I put in more hours than ever, desperate to ignore my internal conflict. All sorts of things were coming back to me, and my memories of Kyle blurred with memories of Mum. I regressed massively in my head, and the strongest memories were suddenly my youngest memories, which wasn't usually the case. I started to remember me and Kyle wearing the same clothes for days on end, cooking our own meals, prodding Mum awake when she'd fallen asleep on the sofa on a Sunday afternoon. Pranking Mrs Crabby. Bus rides with Mum to nowhere, fish-and-chip Fridays, and that grassland. That fresh grassland behind the disused industrial park on the outside of the city. Where Kyle went to — God, Christ, no. Pour me another drink.

The worst flashback of all was of March 1993, Mum in those bloodstained sheets, eyes almost stapled open, cocaine dusting the upturned bin, empty bottles littering the floor. Vibrant red hair spilling over the unwashed pillows and large breasts protruding out of the duvet, her eyes turning to lock into mine, her words to me, cold as night: 'Out. Now.' Even now I tried to tidy up in my mind, put her back to bed, put her chest away, clear up the mess, throw the drugs and booze in the trash along with my awful memories.

I had deep, dark thoughts. Thoughts of hurting myself. Thoughts of saying goodbye like Kyle did.

Simone was in touch regularly, checking I was okay. I sent minimal replies, but I appreciated her contact.

One Saturday afternoon, after a shift at the soft drink factory, I came home to Steph on our sofa, daintily sipping herbal tea. She loved those flavoured teas and I used to pick them up for her on my way home from work, as my bus passed an independent tea store she liked. We'd invested in a really nice mauve sofa and, though I felt it clashed with the walls (though didn't tell Steph that), she looked sweet at this moment, the large cushions swallowing her up inside the plump body of the sofa. She was a slight of a thing, Steph. She never accrued lots of muscle at the gym and always kept a very svelte physique. How could I have not wanted her more, I wonder, looking back. The obvious answer is that I was depressed, though I didn't acknowledge my depression too much at the time. It would take me years to deal with the trauma.

'Can we talk?' She motioned to the mauve armchair opposite, and I tentatively sat down. I too had lost weight, from excessive exercise and work and stress. All the fast food and booze in the world couldn't stop me from shedding pounds at an alarming rate. I had never been overly slim and had a naturally curvy figure with large breasts (much to my own disappointment — they were of little help to me and actually made life a lot more difficult due to their size and weight), but I was definitely my slimmest in October 2006. If I hadn't looked so gaunt and tired in the face you might've thought I was looking my best; unfortunately, my sadness gave the game away.

'I know you're still grieving over Kyle,' she said, 'And your Mum. And so many things.' She pushed her gentle frames delicately up her nose, revealing tears in her big green eyes, 'And I hurt for you and with you. But we weren't okay long before Kyle. You've been losing interest for a long time.'

There was a pause.

'You don't make me feel sexy anymore. We barely have sex. I've needed you. Things have been going on for me, too.'

It's true. Steph's parents were getting a divorce after thirty years of marriage, and she worried a lot for her mum's health. Her mum suffered with severe osteoporosis, having been recently diagnosed after several years of mild to moderate pain. I had been too self-absorbed to help my girlfriend with any of that.

'Is there someone else?' I asked. She rallied at this point, angry at the suggestion.

'Like hell is there someone else,' she retorted indignantly, 'Don't give me the pity party right now. I'm hurting, too.'

It would later transpire that there was someone else, and she would shortly move in with him. Yes, him. A man. An attractive, dark-haired man she'd met through work, who was also a gym bunny. But right now, I didn't know that.

'I think it's over,' she said sadly, 'I think it's been over for a while.'

I would never have broken up with Steph, I don't think. I really did love her, and had been, truly, in love with her. I still fancied her, and I'd still wanted to make it work. But it wasn't to be.

She let me hold on to the flat for a while, but we both agreed we would put it on the market as soon as possible. She moved back in with her parents and not long after with this man. I saw them a few months later together, wandering through Little Portugal, holding hands. He was taller than her, for fuck's sake. I'd always wished I could be taller, and here she was, cavorting merrily with a taller man. I'd be angrier if I wasn't so goddamn sad.

I hung on to the flat for a while, drowning in memories, before realising I was probably better off out of there. Steph left me the portrait of the white deer, and I would sit staring at it for hours. I didn't cry much, mind, not now. I just sat and drank and stared. Looking back, I realise it was similar to what Simone would do before she met Greg — sit and drink and stare for hours on end — but I didn't make the connection at the time. I lost interest in trashy TV, which was unlike me, and kept my friendship circle small: only a handful of trusted comrades could be relied upon to help me through this awful time.

By Christmas 2006 I was out of our flat in Clapham, and by January 2007 I was back in yet another shabby rental place in Brixton, trying to make a cheap rental flat a home.

* * *

140

A couple of years later, mortalled out of my skull on cheap wine (I never did cocaine, not then or since, and didn't do any pot or pills anymore), I saw a familiar face cradled between the backstreets of Vauxhall, near to Cardinals. Fresh under the dirty streetlamp of memory, the Victorian image of Babs emerged, forgotten herself on pills and god knows whatever else. I made an excuse to my lesbian friend Patricia and sidled over to her.

She was sat, old as time, against the graffitied redbrick wall behind her. Her eyes were the same pale grey and her black hair had a salt-and-pepper effect with age. Amazingly, she didn't look too haggard or too worse-for-wear. Her clothes were slightly torn, but she was holding up. Looking up at me, her eyes caught a memory, hardened, confused, wanting to go back to sleep. I saw now the creases in her cheeks, the age in her expression. She furrowed her brows and turned her face away from me.

'Don't you come here,' she cautioned, in her deep, husky voice, a trace of Liverpool still evident, just, through a now-more-London accent, 'Don't you go dragging up old ghosts.'

I did the obvious thing: ask after Mum. Ask after the mum I hadn't known since I was five years old, and knew little of before that. When I asked, I asked the obvious: to know if she's still alive.

'Kid,' she focussed slightly, rallied somewhat, 'I haven't seen your mum in so long.'

My face dropped. I just needed answers.

'She's dead, kid,' she offered, sensing my need. 'She's been dead a long time.'

I told her about Kyle, about how I'd lost him, too. She smiled up.

'Ain't no use crawling in the dirt among bodies that have gone.' It was a vicious image, but it was meant well. 'You can turn it around. Now go, leave me be. Old girls like me need lots of rest.'

It was generous from a woman who probably didn't have much herself, but she had always been compassionate and giving with Kyle and I when we were kids, so it was no surprise. Babs' insight and kindness showed a deeper intelligence: a hidden level of understanding that Kyle and I had never really given her credit for. She could see complexities and emotional resonances that not everyone was attuned enough to pick up on. Had we known more of her past, clues into how Babs had come to learn so many life lessons might have been revealed to us. Like so many women in Kyle's and my lives, though, like Mrs Crabby, Babs, Mum, Simone's mother, Simone to a degree (with her strange little habits and the estranged husband in Norway), Steph in leaving me for a man, Laura, even my friend Janine in choosing to stay with Adam: not everything was revealed. Not everything made sense or added up. Not all of the pieces of the jigsaw seemed to fit together. There were so many questions still left to ask, so many things left to find out, so many obscurities and oddities that would forever, desperately be so. Women would perpetually never make any sense, women would perpetually be enigmas. Hidden from me, hidden from the obvious, hidden from sense, hidden from rational bloody thinking, hidden from life.

I wanted to ask Babs more about Mum: how she'd died, what sort of life she'd led after Kyle and I left, but Babs' face grew suddenly ice-cold, like she didn't want me there anymore, like I'd somehow disturbed the dead. Her eyes glazed over with a pain rooted many years prior; a hurt she'd forced herself over many years to recognise as ambivalence and dust. I nodded goodbye to her and slipped back inside Cardinals, a place I could depend on, out of the frosty cold of the bitter February air and drank with my friends. When it didn't make sense, when I couldn't fill in the blanks, I turned to drink.

After a little while, I realised I should've asked Babs more about Mum and darted back outside into the coolness of night, but she was gone. All these years since, alongside many other regrets, I've always wished I'd asked her just a question or two more.

Hull

March 2021

The pandemic has continued to rage on, and I've mostly sat in my pyjamas when not working, sitting with Baxter and letting the world pass me by. Siobhan had been furloughed from work shortly after our failed date in September 2020 and I'd heard little from her since. She'd returned to Ireland to spend some time with her family. It was hard to stay motivated and I drank a lot again.

Every so often I sat and stared at the portrait of the white deer that Steph had bought for me. It was so beautiful, so regal, so strong. I wanted to be that deer. I wanted to stand alone in the wilderness and be comfortable with that solitude.

Darone had come to me for Christmas. We'd had a good time together, mostly indoors and watching TV. He'd attended a few more of the Black Lives Matter protests after the one I'd known about. I was pleased for him but wondered how any of it would affect me, a white, working-class lesbian in Hull. I was the last thing on anyone's mind.

I thought about moving back to Brixton, where Simone was and where I could rekindle a few old friendships. Up in Hull I only really had Bobby and a couple of other friends. I could do with a larger friendship base. For the time being I suppressed the idea and kept going to work as normal, though it was something

I kept on the backburner as an idea, something I thought I might do eventually. For now, both Baxter and I felt reasonably happy where we were.

One evening in late March I sat on the sofa watching reruns of a couple of my favourite TV shows when a Facebook message came through from my old friend Janine. She'd tried to message a few times over the last five or so years, but I always ignored it. This time I wondered if I might reply. I looked to her profile photo: even after all these years she was still with Adam. I recognised both of their faces anywhere and neither of them looked like they had aged much. Christ. Maybe I wouldn't reply.

I was still speaking to Lara, and she advised that I consider again joining some kind of clubs, just to make a few more friends. I told her I'd think about it. I'd spoken to my GP about depression and he'd suggested some antidepressants. I'd told him I wasn't ready, and here we were. A pack of mild antidepressants sat on my coffee table: the doctor said I could start taking them if I wanted to but there wasn't any immediate risk to me without them. I decided to leave them well alone for the time being but kept hold of them, just in case.

Another thing Lara advised was to take the painting of the white deer down and bin it. It was the last day of March 2021 and I had finished watching TV, the painting on full display behind the television set. I didn't want to take it down, but I figured I probably should, understanding Lara's angle. The portrait will only ever remind me of Steph, she said. It will only ever make me sad. I should start trying to be happy.

I poured Baxter a few dog biscuits and reached up to the fixture on the wall. I'd put on a bit of weight since Christmas and my arms didn't look as defined as they had done. I made a mental note to get back to the gym once they opened again in a week or so, build myself back up again. I gently lifted the portrait from its nail in the wall, held it in my arms for a few moments, looked again into the deer's eyes. Sad, black, hollow eyes like mine. I looked long into the deer's eyes and remembered Kyle's eyes when we went to try to find Mum: how they bulged with anticipation and wildness. This deer's eyes were not wild. They were like mine, tamed and oppressed. This was not a wild deer after all. This was a prisoner like me.

I took the deer to the rubbish outside, using a hammer to break it up completely. I cried with each hit, my pain and my anger unleashed all at once. I didn't care what the neighbours heard. I just wanted release. The painting splintered into thousands of pieces like the castaway fragments of my broken heart.

I thought of messaging Siobhan again, maybe I could be open with her now. I turned my phone off and went to bed.

That night, under the feral stars of the midnight sky, I dreamt of a knock at the door. When I answered, she was there, all red hair billowing down, fresh-faced, dressed to the nines, not a day over thirty.

'Chrissy-Wissy,' she teased, her eyes coal black as the heavens around her. 'Ain't you gonna offer an old girl a drink?'

And just like that, with minimal effort, she almost got her own way one last time.

Maelstrom

Fires and roses
In equal measures
Strip us of
Our greatest pleasures.
The maelstrom comes:
It takes you blind.
There was a time
When you were mine.